D1603678

THE 2000-MILE TURTLE

Truth crushed to earth frequently just
lies there, thank God.

HAROLD SMITH

The 2000-Mile Turtle

and other episodes from
Editor Harold Smith's
Private Journal

H.B. FOX

MADRONA PRESS, INC.
AUSTIN, TEXAS

ISBN 0–89052–014–3

Library of Congress Catalog Card No. 75–1600
Copyright © 1975 by H. B. Fox
All Rights Reserved

Second Printing 1975

Manufactured in the United States of America

CONTENTS

NOTICE

This book, except for some obvious whoppers, occasionally is true, in an un-pin-downable sort of way, but the names have been changed to protect the guilty.

H.B. FOX

I

Congressman Caxton's Downfall

I read the letter, smiled just a fraction, and dropped it in the wastebasket. I picked up the *Dallas News* from the stack on my desk and was leaning back resting my mind on the editorial page when the idea hit me. It was one of those times you bust out laughing at an idea that leaps into your brain ready-formed and raring to be done.

The letter was from my congressman, the Honorable Nat Caxton, Washington, D.C., and the reason I'd got it was on account of me tearing my pants two weeks before. I'd better explain.

I had walked back to the press room, where Clyde was printing that week's *Gazette* on the Babcock flatbed. Standing on tiptoe near the flywheel to yell to him above the clatter of the press—I think it was to tell him a slug had worked up between the lines of type and was smudging the papers—I leaned over a little too far and my pants leg caught in a belt. I got a bad cut on the knee. Wasn't serious, but like any columnist, or novelist, for that matter, who keeps writing when he's got nothing to say, I wrote a little piece for my personal column on the hazards of editing; said an editor could tear his pants on the *Oat Hill Gazette* the same as he could on the *Dallas News* or the *Houston Post*.

By the middle of the following week I had this letter from Congressman Nat Caxton on official U.S. Congress stationery, sympathizing with me and congratulating me on not getting hurt seriously. "I think you're putting out a fine little paper, I never miss an issue," Nat wrote. "The strength of this nation is based on freedom of the press. Communism will never prevail as long as we have editors like you standing up for the truth.'' He also threw in a good word for my wife, whom he called the little woman.

Why should a United States congressman be writing a letter of condolence for a cut knee to the editor of a two-by-four country weekly? When the country is fraught with peril, both foreign and domestic? At least everybody's saying so. You'll see.

Congressman Nat Caxton, or as it was sometimes spelled in free democratic spirit, *Gnat* Caxton, had got to Washington, to a seat in the councils of the world's most powerful government, the same way Warren Harding once became the head of it. Sheer luck, combined with the occasional waywardness of the democratic process.

Nat had got his start in politics by preferring handshaking to hand hoeing. His first elective office after leaving the farm was justice of the peace in Castorville, two counties over from Oat Hill, which he won by a majority of six over a retired Baptist preacher running on a platform of international Prohibition and immediate bombing of Russia and China unless they turned to God. Nat merely shook hands with everybody—a strategy that's hard to beat, regardless of what office you're running for, as Lyndon Johnson demonstrated.

The F.B.I. is said, by the F.B.I., rarely to turn over to the courts a man who isn't guilty. The constable in Judge Caxton's precinct was better than that. Under the fee system then in use, a justice of the peace's salary was a percentage of the fines he levied. No conviction, no fine; no fine, no fee. The record in Nat's court: 100 percent convictions. You might jump to the conclusion that this strained Nat's relationship with his friends, but it didn't. His friends never were charged.

Due, however, to an upsurge of church revivals and East Texas undernourishment, crime slowed in his area and Nat's salary nosedived. When it sank to forty dollars a month, Nat knew he had a problem. It was run for something else or go to work. Nat ran. For a seat in the Texas Legislature, when the annual salary was twelve hundred dollars, you worked only about three months every two years, and nobody else in his district wanted the job. He won hands down and showed up in Austin with hands out, but nobody noticed. There's money to be made in the state government in Texas; in fact, any governor or member of the House or Senate who doesn't come out richer than he went in is considered by his colleagues to be incompetent. But the usufructs of office are hard to come by when you're fifteen members away from the chairmanship of a single committee, and Nat grew restive.

In his fourth year in the Legislature the state was redistricted and Nat, seizing the opportunity, gerrymandered a new U.S. congressional bailiwick that snaked around through this part of the state, taking in all his kinfolks and hangers-on, and the following year he ran for Congress and got elected—something he hadn't even had the nerve to dream about when he was justice of the peace.

In Washington, Congressman Caxton wasn't very interested in or aware of international affairs, the national budget, the economic index, or the chairmanship of the Appropriations Committee. Washington was a hundred times further than he had ever calculated on getting and he settled down to staying there. The salary suited him fine, the hours were good, spittoons were furnished, the bean soup in the House restaurant was delicious, and free haircuts were no more than a public servant deserved. This was a good country, he had a top-notch job, and he aimed to stay there.

But Nat made one mistake. He was too thorough. (Beware the man who is too attentive to his wife.) While he sent his constituents all the free seeds he could get hold of in Washington and held the record four years straight for sending out the most copies of the Agricultural Yearbook—each one personally autographed by him, meaning his secretary—he wasn't content with the ordinary. He figured out a system he estimated would keep him in Congress from then on.

He subscribed to every weekly newspaper in his district, all twenty-eight of them, the *Gazette* included. Then he assigned one secretary to do nothing but read all those papers, glean all the names she could, and give him a typed summary of why the names appeared in the news.

If somebody in the district got married, Congressman Caxton immediately sent the couple a letter of congratulations and a complimentary pass to the House of Representatives. When you take into account that most weddings in a rural district are not heralded as social highlights by the big dailies, you can see that getting a personal letter from their congressman in far-off Washington left a mighty warm feeling in the hearts of the bridal couples. It gave them something to talk about along about the time they'd discovered there wasn't much to talk about, say the second or third day of marriage.

If somebody died, the survivors immediately received a sympathy letter. The letters all read pretty much alike but there's not too much originality can be worked into a message to the bereaved. If somebody fell off a ladder and was laid up a week in the hospital, a letter from the congressman was on the way as soon as that fellow's hometown paper reached Washington. "Well, I'll be darned, that was nice of Nat," the voter would say.

Whatever a man had, good luck or bad, a broken leg, a new water well, a prize at the fair, the first bale of cotton, or twin calves, if his name got into a weekly paper in the district, he got a warm personal letter from Nat. Nobody's ever gotten mad at getting a personal letter bragging on him if he's achieved something or feeling sorry for him if he's lost something.

In an average year, Congressman Caxton figured, he was writing five thousand personal letters to his constituents, and he believed the system was building up a backlog of affection that would keep him in office permanently.

You see now why I got the letter about my cut knee and torn pants.

That week when the press run for the *Gazette* was completed, Clyde stopped the Babcock, lifted off the front-page form and carried it over to the make-up stone. I unlocked the form and started taking out type while Clyde, still wondering if I knew what I was doing, brought over a couple of galleys of new type, complete with headlines. We put this new type in, locked up the page, put it back on the press, and ran off half a dozen copies.

I took five of them up to my office and put them in my safe. The other one was carefully wrapped and addressed to the Honorable Nat Caxton, M.C., House Office Building, Washington, D.C., and, after making sure the regular copy that would have gone to him didn't, I dropped the special one in the mail sack along with the other papers.

What I had done was sort of tamper with the news a little in that special copy going to the congressman. About half the leading citizens of Oat Hill were reported as having been in some mishap or were in "the news" for one reason or another.

Arthur and Agnes Struthers, who had been married something like thirty-five years but had no children, were reported to have a new son, whom they'd named Nat Caxton Struthers. Banker Jonathon Carp, having stepped off the curb in front of the bank while reaching for a quarter he'd spotted, had fallen and broken his right leg. All the drug stock of M. A. Jackson was reported lost in a disastrous fire that had swept the south side of the courthouse square, also damaging the Butler Variety Store and the Blue Bonnet Cafe. The other three sides of the square were saved only by the heroic efforts of the Oat Hill Volunteer Fire Department. Fire Chief Sam Brady, overcome by heat and smoke while manning a fire hose, was recovering. John Honeycut, Oat Hill's sixty-eight-year-old bachelor, was reported married to a young widow from Houston and was building a new home. Crawford Jones, who farms three miles south of town, was gored by his bull. Jimmie Hines, who had dropped out of high school two years before because he found racking balls at Dick's Pool Hall more fascinating, was reported valedictorian of his class.

Well, you can imagine the shock and confusion when, along about the middle of the next week, letters started arriving in Oat Hill from Congressman Caxton.

"Dear Jonathon," the letter to Banker Carp began. "Awfully sorry to learn of your painful accident, but hope the bone is now mending satisfactorily and you can be back in your office before too long. The country needs sound, conservative banking like you're furnishing the good people of Altha County."

"What accident is he talking about?" Banker Carp sputtered. "Mending bones? What's gone wrong with that lightweight we got in Washington?"

"Fire?" Chief Brady wanted to know. "We haven't had a fire here in three months."

"New home?" Bachelor Honeycut bellowed. "Married! Why, they better take ole Nat out and have his head examined. I'm still

5

living in the Roberts Hotel where I been living for forty-five years and I ain't married and don't intend to be."

"I wouldn't name a pet coon after him," Arthur Struthers declared.

"I ain't even got a bull," Farmer Crawford Jones said when he brought his letter to town to see what it meant.

And what was said around at the pool hall about the letter congratulating Jimmie Hines on his fine scholastic record is not news that's fit to print, except in *Harper's* or the *Atlantic Monthly*.

No use enumerating all of them, but about thirty-five or forty people around Oat Hill were either hopping mad or splitting their sides laughing over those crazy, haywire letters from Congressman Caxton. And the following week, when I carried a big story in the *Gazette* about it and took my copies of the doctored edition out of the safe and showed them around town, the word spread, and Congressman Caxton became the laughingstock of his district.

Needless to say it certainly destroyed the congressman's confidence in the press. Not knowing when some other paper was going to double-cross him, he was left with nothing much to do in Washington but eat bean soup.

Well, it beat him. A politician can survive nearly anything except being hooted at. If he'd stuck to seed and Agricultural Yearbooks he might have been there yet. Lots of others no better qualified are.

Last I heard of Nat, he was running for justice of the peace once more over in Castorville; said his Washington background and familiarity with sessions of the Supreme Court, which he had visited on several occasions, equipped him for real service in the justice of the peace court. I hope he gets elected.

2

The Competing Post Office

I was arguing with a friend in the Blue Bonnet Cafe the other day that the ratio of smart people to dumb ones in a small town is about the same as it is in a city.

I have a notion that the gradations in the level of intelligence in Congress, for example, are about the same as in the Oat Hill Chamber of Commerce. There are some smart, civilized, capable, hardworking men, and some incompetents and boobs, in both. As for crooks, Congress may have the edge; at least there are more congressmen in jail, perhaps due solely to larger opportunities, the rule being that crookedness in the human breast expands in proportion to the opportunities available. There are always more honest clerks in a store using cash registers than in one making change out of a cigar box. There aren't any cash registers in Congress.

I have watched business tycoons, educators, political leaders, and writers on television, and it seems to me it doesn't take any more intelligence to succeed in business, school-teaching, plumbing, writing, politics, or barbering in New York, say, than it does in Oat Hill. Add four or five zeroes to the promissory note and Jonathon Carp of the Farmers State Bank in Oat Hill would be banking on the New York level. The principle of banking is the same whether you're lending $500 or $500,000—you've got to get the money back with interest.

Astute historians and, more dependably, the rest of us who watched Harry Truman now regard him as an outstanding President, but he had the same intelligence in the White House he had in the courthouse, when he was a county judge in Missouri. There must be hundreds of county judges right now—well dozens anyway, excusing the one we've got here—who, if pushed up through luck and circumstances to the U.S. Senate and then into the White House, would make very creditable Presidents. The fact that they stay on as county judges doesn't make them lesser men, just lesser known. Most governors, congressmen and senators are like popular singers now in the current limelight: they didn't get to stardom because their voices are any better than thousands of others singing away on the back rows of church choirs, but purely through happenstance and canny promotion.

The difference in intelligence between U.S. congressmen and Oat Hill city councilmen is scarcely measurable. The children of one usually amount to about as much as the children of the other. You won't be any better able to name a single current congressman thirty years hence than you can an Oat Hill councilman now.

I have a theory that if you know fifty or seventy-five of your contemporaries real well plus about that many you've met through books, newspapers, and magazines, you know everybody on earth.

I'd like you to know Debbs Craig, the Oat Hill citizen who got mad at the federal government one time and put in his own post office, making ours the only town in the United States with two at the same time.

It was in the days when few towns had federal buildings and the national debt was still under fifty billion. The government didn't put up a post office building that everybody went around thanking their congressman for in a town the size of Oat Hill; it just rented a vacant building from a free enterpriser and built a partition down the middle, lined it with lock boxes, sawed out a window, covered it with grilled bars, and put in some rusty pens and dried ink, and that was the post office. Not swanky, but it'd handle a letter from New York or Washington as smoothly as any we've got now, only a day or two faster. People in Oat Hill got their income tax notices as soon as anybody in Dallas, and waited as long to fill them out.

One fall it came time to make a new rental contract on the post office building in Oat Hill. Albert Barton, the postmaster, wanted the post office to stay where it was, in a building owned by his wife's cousin. But Debbs Craig wanted it in a vacant building he owned. Renting to the government was a pretty satisfactory deal after the red tape was behind you. Wasn't any worry about collecting the rent, and the tenant wasn't always trying to get you to lower the price.

Now Debbs wasn't any ordinary man and I ought to tell you something about him before I get on with the post-office matter. He was the most independent nonmillionaire Texan I ever saw. People in small towns, like people in cities or suburbs or riding around the country in trailer houses, are sometimes so opinionless and supine, lest they rub somebody the wrong way or lose a customer, offend a minority, or be thought different or guilty of thinking at all, that they're about as exhilarating as a lecturer before the PTA or a governor of a doubtful state seconding the nomination of a candidate for President of the United States.

Not Debbs. He did *what* he pleased, *like* he pleased, *when* he pleased, and he made money and came out financially independent, in a small-town way. The difference between a financially independent man in a small town and a big operator in a city is that the former operates on his own money, while the latter borrows.

Debbs was running a dry-goods store after the First World War when money was flowing good and loud silk shirts were popular among the dudes. One day a farmer came into his store on the square in Oat Hill and slammed a bundle on the counter.

"What's this?" Debbs asked.

"It's that shirt I bought here yesterday," the farmer said. "I'm bringing it back."

"What's the matter with it?"

"Nothing."

"What're you bringing it back for then?"

"Just don't like it, that's all."

Debbs scowled. Returning merchandise for no reason at all might be all right for those big Dallas stores, but he didn't go for it.

"Just a minute now, let's see about this." He opened the package and unfolded the loudest striped silk shirt you ever saw. The green stripes in it must have been an inch wide, separated by purple and yellow dots. He held it up to the light, taking a good long look at it.

"You sure you don't like it?" he asked.

"I'm sure," the farmer said.

"Well, by God, I don't like it either." And he ripped it into shreds and threw it on the floor. "Here's your money back." He said the man who made it ought to have something or other cut out.

Another time, after Debbs had retired from his dry-goods store and had plenty of spare time, the town elected him mayor. He didn't want the job, never shook hands in his life with anybody he wasn't personally glad to see, and figured he wasn't qualified. But the people in Oat Hill just put his name on the ballot and elected him anyway, so he gave in and agreed to serve.

The first week in office, hunting around for something for a mayor to do, Debbs decided he was going to straighten out the parking problem around the courthouse square. Like it was, people just drove up and parked, regardless of which direction they were coming from, right side or left side of the street, north or south, east or west, it didn't matter. See an open place at the curb and dart in.

"No sense in such a jumble." Debbs decided. "Ought to have some order like they do in Houston, make room for more cars."

He bought a can of white paint, got a helper, and, late at night, around eight-thirty when all the cars were off the street, painted neat stripes on the pavement at the proper angle and spacing so all cars would be parked alike around the square.

Next morning Mayor Craig came downtown rubbing his hands with satisfaction over a job well done. His wasn't going to be a do-nothing administration.

When he got to the square, his face fell, then turned purple. Cars and pickups were parked like they'd always been, across the stripes, on top of them, at the wrong angle. Worst mess you ever saw. Looked like some people had gone out of their way to park the wrong way across Debbs' stripes.

Debbs took a second look, wheeled around; stalked into the city secretary's office, and wrote out a check for one hundred dollars.

"Here," he said to Miss Orene, "this'll pay for another election. I'm resigning. I won't be mayor for no such damned fools."

Everybody promised to do better and park right, but what Debbs said they could do to themselves isn't printable, not in Oat Hill. In literary circles in New York it could be said at a dinner party. Take Norman Mailer, for example. I've often wondered, if he doesn't think there's such a thing as crudity, why doesn't he save his friends a lot of steps by installing a commode in the middle of his living room?

Another sore spot with Debbs was Jim Ferguson, rest his soul, the Texas governor who had some trouble with an investigating committee over some money he couldn't explain and got impeached and barred from holding office in the state ever again. Debbs didn't like him before he got into trouble and liked him less when Governor Jim turned around and ran his wife, Ma Ferguson, for governor. "Two Governors for the price of one," sly ole Jim kept saying. It worked and she got elected, but Debbs hadn't believed it could happen.

"People of Texas got too much sense to elect a woman governor," he had argued. "Biggest fool notion I ever heard of."

The morning after the election—there wasn't any radio or television news in those days—Debbs came downtown and walked into the Blue Bonnet Cafe.

"How'd the election come out?" he asked. "How bad'd she get beat?"

"Why, Ma Ferguson won," he was told.

"Naw. Impossible. People of Texas got more sense. . . ."

"Here, look at the paper." They showed him the headline in the *Houston Post:* MA FERGUSON ELECTED.

That's all he read. He whirled around, walked out on the street, pulled out his watch, looked at it sharply, shook it, held it up to his ear, and discovered it had stopped running.

"By God!" he spit the words out. "That's the last time you'll ever stop running!"

And he smashed the watch down on the sidewalk, breaking it into smithereens, and walked off without looking back.

As far as I know, the matter was never brought up in Debbs' presence, anymore than anybody ever mentioned to him the time when, after he'd bought his first radio and a bunch of static came on in the middle of a program he was listening to, he picked it up and threw it out a window, which was closed at the time.

Once Debbs demonstrated his independence in church. He was a Methodist and he liked for the preacher to finish his sermon exactly at twelve noon. That's the time he ate.

One Sunday morning Debbs and his wife, Opal, were sitting in their regular places down near the front on an aisle and along about a quarter of twelve the preacher was still going strong. You could see he was going to overshoot twelve by a considerable amount, and Debbs began to fidget. At five minutes to twelve he pulled out his watch—this was before Ma Ferguson's election—held it up close to his face for a good look, shook it, shifted his head from side to side to get the thing in proper focus, wound it ostentatiously, scowled at Opal, and put the watch back in his pocket. Opal kept looking straight ahead at the preacher, enjoying the sermon on the need for Prohibition in France. At twelve sharp Debbs began twisting and turning more. He coughed a few times, louder than necessary. Opal nudged him, trying to shush him, but he wouldn't shush. "It's twelve o'clock," he muttered sideways to her. "Time to go."

"He'll be through in a little bit. You be still," Opal whispered back. They drink a lot of wine in France and you can't dry them up in fifteen minutes.

"Ain't no sense in preaching that long," Debbs said through his teeth. "He's already said all he's got to say. Everybody here agrees with him. Ain't no Frenchmen around. Let's go. Time to eat dinner."

Opal looked straight ahead.

Debbs pulled out his watch again. It was ten after twelve. He couldn't stand it any longer.

"I'm going," he said and coughed again, got up while putting his watch back into his pocket, and stalked up the aisle and out the door.

Now among the congregation there might have been several different interpretations put on Debbs' action. Maybe he had a sick cow, or wasn't feeling good himself, or he'd remembered he'd left the water running in the bathroom.

Debbs cleared up all such misconceptions. When he got outside he climbed into his car, got under the wheel, started the motor, and began honking the horn. It wasn't any timid, accidental toot; it was a loud, prolonged, insistent series of blasts, unmistakably sounded by an impatient man honking for his wife, and heard all over the church. It was clear and unarguable, especially to the preacher, who wound up his sermon two pages shy with France still a third wet, called for one verse of Beulah Land, gave the benediction like a modern radio announcer trying to get all the weather report in before his time runs out, and dismissed the congregation.

The following Sunday and thereafter, he finished at 11:59. Debbs was not only a faithful member; he was also a heavy contributor.

You get the idea of what kind of man Debbs Craig was. And when the contract for the post office building went once more to Postmaster Albert Barton's wife's cousin, Debbs naturally didn't like it, particularly since he was low bidder. Albert claimed the slightly higher rent in his wife's cousin's building was more than offset by the added convenience the building gave. The only convenience Debbs could detect was to Albert's wife's cousin, and he attributed the final decision to whom it belonged. Albert had worked hard to elect Nat Caxton to Congress. Nat believed in keeping things in the family; had his own wife and two kids and some in-laws on the congressional payroll himself.

Debbs probably would have let matters slide with the remark that if he had to get into politics to rent a building he'd let it go vacant from now on, but Albert Barton wasn't the kind to let well enough alone. He kept rubbing it in. I guess a man does get bored being postmaster. Must be like acting in the same play on Broadway every night for three years.

"Well, see your building's still vacant," he'd say when he met Debbs on the street, especially if there were a few listeners standing around. "Trouble with you is you just ain't got enough influence in Washington, that's all." He'd cackle and rub his hands.

The fourth time Albert mentioned his lack of influence in Washington Debbs got an idea. "I'll show that small-time politician what influence is," he said.

What he decided to do was open up a competing post office. It's a free country, he told himself and guffawed silently, if you can do that.

Debbs got a saw and a hammer, hired a helper, built a partition down the middle of his vacant building, sawed out a window, tacked some mesh wire across the top half of it, put a stool behind it, and went into business. First he bought a quarter-page advertisement in the *Oat Hill Gazette*:

Announcing . . .

A NEW POST OFFICE

For Oat Hill.

No Red Tape Here.

Prompt, Courteous Service.

Will Appreciate Your Business.

SPECIAL FOR OPENING DAY:

30 one-cent stamps for 25¢

Limit 30 to a Customer.

DEBBS CRAIG

Sole owner

"What in the world is ole Debbs up to? He lost his mind?" people began asking when the paper came out. When they went by his building and saw his sign—"Private Post Office, Oat Hill, Texas"—they were speechless, which in a small town, the same as in Washington, means they talked a lot.

But Debbs didn't say much.

"Competition, that's what it is," he'd say. "This country is based on competitive free enterprise. Government's had a monopoly on the mail long enough. It's a free country, ain't it?"

"But, Debbs, how you gonna operate?" Bill Anderson, the plumber, demanded. "Post office department ain't gonna cooperate with you."

"You got a letter to mail? Mail it right there in that slot and see."

Bill did and, sure enough, in a few days he got an answer to his letter from the plumbing supply house he'd sent it to in Houston, only the answer came back through the regular post office. He spread the word: Debbs' post office was working.

Other folks started dropping in, especially after Debbs offered a free apple with each parcel-post package mailed.

"But what about incoming mail?" Bill Anderson wanted to know. "When you gonna handle that too? Like to have a box here."

"Well, I haven't worked out the details on that yet," Debbs said. "Let ole Albert handle that in his post office. I don't want *all* the business. Monopolistic. Besides, the money's in the outgoing end of the business. Incoming mail, some other postmaster up the line's already got the gravy on that."

Well, naturally, there were a good many folks in Oat Hill who didn't like Postmaster Albert Barton. A lot of them had wanted his job, or their kinfolks had. A lot of people just liked Debbs and wanted to egg him on to see what would happen. So business was picking up steadily at Debbs' post office and dropping fast at Albert's. Before long a government postal inspector showed up in Oat Hill.

"What's the matter, Albert?" he asked the postmaster. "Been going over the receipt figures. How come your volume is falling off so much here? Rate you're going, you'll have this post office back to third class before long. Guess you know that'd mean a cut in salary. Don't understand it. Other towns around here doing more'n they've ever done."

"I know it. I can't help it," Albert blurted out. "I, well, uh, I got competition!"

"Competition? Thunderation, there's no such thing in this business. You need a rest?"

Albert was sweating all over. "Come on, I'll show you."

He slammed his hat on and led the inspector out the door and down the street to Debbs' post office. "Take a look." He pointed to the sign, "Private Post Office."

The inspector's eyes bulged and he hurried inside.

"Morning," Debbs said from behind his window, figuring right off who the man was, what with Albert in tow. "What can I do for you? Need some stamps? Got some pretty new green ones this morning. Mail a package? Get a fresh Winesap apple this week with each package mailed. Believe they pull in more business than those Delicious varieties. What kind *you* giving away, Albert?"

15

The inspector was near the exploding point.

"Look here, mister," he said. "I'm from the United States Post Office Department." He showed his credentials.

"Glad to make your acquaintance," Debbs said. "But I won't be needing any of your services. I'm not affiliated with your organization. Stand back just a minute. Got a customer. Customers come ahead of traveling salesmen in this establishment. Jaw with you two gentlemen later."

He sold a three-cent stamp to Miss Anna Drake. "Just a minute, Miss Anna," he said. "I'll put that stamp on for you." Debbs licked the stamp, stuck it on, and tossed the letter in a pouch marked OUT-GOING. "Got any packages, bring em in, my scales are just as honest as the government's. And take an apple in advance." Miss Anna thanked him and went out munching.

"What're you going to do with that letter?" The inspector had pushed back up to the window.

"Dispatch it," Debbs said.

"Where's it going?"

"Confidential. Private matter. You'll have to ask Miss Anna if she wants that information given out."

"Look here now. You can't do this."

"Yeah, but I'm doing it." Debbs looked him in the eyes.

"You know you can be arrested?"

"Sure. So can you. So can anybody. If they break the law. Not against the law to accommodate people, is it? No law against licking stamps and giving away apples, is there?"

The inspector pulled himself together and tried another tack.

"Now, Mr. . . . er—"

"Craig's the name. Debbs Craig."

"Now, Mr. Craig, you know and I know you don't deliver those letters individually all over the country. Where do you carry them to put them in the U.S. mail?"

"Different places. Sometimes to Prairieville, sometimes to Hemp-ville, Castorville, wherever I feel like going. Any place but around to ole Albert's post office here. He hasn't canceled a one of my stamps yet. Buy all my stamps out of town, too. How's *your* business, Albert? Falling off any?''

Albert squirmed.

"But, Mr. Craig," the inspector put in, "you're losing money at it.''

Debbs looked at him and sort of grinned: "Your outfit making any money?''

The inspector fell back like he'd been slapped. "Well, no, of course not, but that's different.''

"No different to me. I got a long way to go before my deficit's as big as yours.''

The inspector, mad again, was stumped. "You'll be hearing from the government about this. You can't get away with it, whatever it is you're up to. Silliest thing I ever heard of.'' He wheeled around and walked out, Albert right on his heels. First time he'd ever encountered such a problem. There wasn't anything in the P.O. Rules and Regulations covering it. He'd have to check higher up.

Well, it wasn't long before Congressman Nat Caxton eased down from Washington and into Oat Hill after dark and got hold of Debbs at his home.

"Look, Debbs," he said, "you're messing things up around here. Got the Post Office Department the laughing stock of this area. Not doing me any good either. Now Albert Barton is a good man, a useful man, did me a lot of good in the campaign. Can't we iron this thing out sensible? What you got in mind, Debbs?''

"Well, I'll tell you," Debbs said, speaking low. They talked for about five minutes.

"Uh-huh," Congressman Nat said. "Uh-huh. I see. That's possible. I believe in the low bid, too. You shut this thing down and we'll see about it.''

Next morning Debbs put up a sign on his post office: CLOSED FOR REPAIRS. He sat back and waited.

Two weeks later carpenters and painters were busy sprucing up the Debbs Craig building, plastering the walls, painting the woodwork, and sanding the floors. A week later an announcement on the door said: "After the first of the month this will be the new location of the Oat Hill U.S. Post Office. [Signed] Albert Barton, P.M."

Albert explained around town that the old post-office building was leaking and the government had decided to move; you know how those Washington bureaucrats are. Sometimes, when your own job is at stake, your wife's cousin has to fight his own battles.

Debbs told me he lost only $185 on apples and $231 selling 30 cents' worth of stamps for 25 cents. He was going to those other towns anyway; might as well be hauling packages and letters. The new lease with the government was for five years and likely to be renewed at the end of that time, and he'd have his money back after the first six months.

This country is still full of ingenuity, except maybe when it comes to foreign policy.

3

Birth of the *Gazette*

I've got ahead of myself, so before I go any farther I ought to stop and say I didn't inherit the *Gazette* and I didn't buy it. I thought it up, the same as Einstein did the atom bomb and Edison the light bulb. Einstein is reported to have said that if he had it to do over again he wouldn't do it; he'd have been a plumber instead. I've crawled under a house in the dead of winter to fix a busted pipe and if I had it to do over again I'd still be an editor.

When I got out of college I knew I wanted to be a newspaperman, but I didn't want to work for a big daily; I wanted to run my own weekly. Considering my financial resources, the only way was to start one. Here's how I did it.

One spring morning I walked into the Farmers State Bank in Oat Hill, pushed through the swinging half-door of the president's office, and paused.

The president looked up over the top of his glasses.

"Something for you?"

"Are you Mr. Carp?"

"Yes."

"My name is Harold Smith."

"Yes. What can I do for you, Mr. Smith?"

He hadn't asked me to sit, but I sat down in the chair in front of his desk. "Nothing, really. Just wanted to talk to you."

"What about?" There are two kinds of people a banker is automatically wary of: a stranger and a friend who's overborrowed and overdrawn.

"Well, I wanted to get your opinion."

"What about?"

"I'm thinking of starting a newspaper here and. . . ."

"Don't think much of it." He cut in before I could finish.

"Why not, Mr. Carp?"

"We already got one."

"You don't think there's room for another?"

"No."

"Two banks here, aren't there?" The First National was on the other side of the courthouse square.

"That's different."

"Both making money, aren't they?"

"Maybe so. This one is."

"Wouldn't one hold all the money this town's got?"

"Don't follow you, young man. What're you driving at?"

"I figure if a town can support two banks, even if one could do the job alone, it can support two newspapers."

"Well, it's a free country. You're entitled to your opinion. You might find Clayton Martin mighty tough competition though."

I knew who Clayton Martin was. Like a Kennedy planning a presidential campaign, I had studied Oat Hill minutely, had memorized the names of most of the leading citizens, and knew their occupations, as well as their church affiliations. Clayton Martin was, and had been for twenty years, the owner and editor of the *Oat Hill News*, he was a deacon in the Baptist Church, he wouldn't accept liquor advertising, and he banked at the Farmers State.

"Won't take up any more of your time, Mr. Carp. Just wanted to get acquainted. Thank you." I got up and left.

An enterprise as unmirthful as Mr. Carp's, I figured, needed jollying up a little and the next day, just to be doing, I opened a small account at his bank and while the transaction was going on I eased a quarter out of my pocket and slid it under the change-making machine at the teller's window.

If you know anything about banking, outside the fact that you get a notice to come in at once if you're overdrawn, you know that in a town like Oat Hill or San Francisco the bank usually has a couple of false Grecian columns plastered to the outside of the building to help hold up the president's idea that a bank is more cultured than a grocery store. You also know there is a banking rite called balancing the cash, which is far more sacred than Holy Communion to a Methodist. Pick out a bank, any bank, the Farmers State in Oat Hill or the Chase Manhattan in New York, and go in at a certain time any day in the week and you'll find the clerks devoted to their pious tasks of balancing the cash.

Now you and me, if we thought we had $5.35 in our pocket and pulled it out to make sure we had enough to stop by the cafe for supper and a picture show afterwards and counted only $5.25, we'd shrug and go on about our business; but a bank, it'll turn itself upside down before it'll allow a dime to go unaccounted for, even when it's a dime ahead.

"That's even worse," Banker Carp always pointed out. "*Much* worse. You show up a dime ahead and it means some customer was shorted, and the integrity of the institution is at stake."

If most people's integrity hinges on how well they can keep up with loose change, the amount of integrity in this world is about like I had it figured.

Jonathon Carp and his two tellers worked overtime that afternoon trying to account for that quarter. To me, it was money well spent.

I'm not sure I had exactly leveled with Jonathon Carp in that first meeting. I wasn't just *thinking* of starting a newspaper in Oat Hill. At that moment a truck carrying a second-hand Babcock flatbed press, a beat-up Model 8 Linotype, an eight by ten job press, a paper cutter, make-up stones, type cases, a roll-top desk, and other items a careful novelist would list to prove he had researched his field, was leaving Houston, a hundred miles away, headed for Oat Hill.

By five o'clock of that still, sunny day I had visited most of the stores around the courthouse square, introduced myself, discussed the economic possibilities of a second newspaper in Oat Hill, been encouraged or discouraged in proportion to how much the man I was talking to disliked or liked Editor Clayton Martin. I also had stopped by the Texas Power and Light Company to pay a meter deposit and have the electricity turned on at the building I'd rented from Jim

Bowers on the southeast corner of the square. I then went to the Blue Bonnet Cafe to eat and wait for the truck.

I won't bother you with the details; unloading printing machinery is a backbreaking job; importing a printer and getting him a place to stay takes time; getting out the first issue of a weekly newspaper is arduous and nerve-wracking, especially in a town that really doesn't care whether you get one out or not. These things have nothing to do with my story, which tells how I launched a small-town newspaper successfully and reached financial security on the back of a turtle.

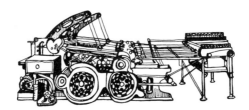

4

The Turtle

What difference does it make whether it was a hot day in July or a windy day in March? I would have done it anyway. Still, whoever heard of a piece of literature that wasn't crammed with weather reports every 15 or 20 pages and long descriptions of rolling countryside or wistful city streets (I remember Ray Sheffield's telling me when he and I were 12, "Say, you ought to read this book, it starts out with conversation and ain't got a long description in it.") So, to get it over with, I'll tell you it was 3 o'clock in the afternoon on a Thursday in June, the paper was out, the temperature was 72 degrees, and the sun was shining with rain-washed brilliance on the courthouse square of Oat Hill, Texas, population, 3,040, county seat of Altha, population 15,960. I came out of the *Gazette* office, pulled my hat down against the glare, and left for a walk in the country.

I was going thinking. I was in trouble. Not woman trouble—this is not that kind of book. If you're fascinated with spectator sex, go to a movie or read a best seller. For me, reading about sex is as insubstantial as reading about good food. My trouble was financial, which is the worst kind, responsible for 90 percent of the world's ills, domestic and foreign, physical and mental, real and poetic, white or black.

"Harold, you're getting out a mighty good little paper," Burt Johnson had said earlier in the week, standing behind the meat counter wiping his hands on his apron and smelling like a grocery store.

"In fact, it's the newsiest paper Oat Hill ever had," Burt went on, "but you've got to have more readers before I can advertise in it."

For the sixteenth week in a row Burt had declined to advertise his Friday and Saturday specials in the *Gazette*. "I'll just have to stick with the *News* till you get more subscribers."

The trouble with this, like my notion that man isn't capable of managing this world, was it was the truth. Business is business. General Motors and I know that. I wouldn't have advertised in the *Gazette* either. Only 301 subscribers. In a town of more than 3,000, a county of over 15,000.

It was now eleven months since I'd started the *Gazette*, against the advice of banker Jonathon Carp, with three thousand dollars worth of second-hand printing equipment. I'd used up my initial capital and now was at the point of having to make it pay or give up. I could make it pay if I had more advertising, and I could get more advertising if I had more subscribers. It was sort of like the Negroes in Mississippi. Whites won't associate with them till they get better educated and they can't get better educated till they're associated with. I said Mississippi but I could just as well have said Washington or Harlem or Watts or the ghetto in Detroit. Anyway, I was going broke, with nobody to picket because of it.

I walked through the business district—which slick-magazine writers would describe here but I'll do it later—and out the residential street where I had a room at Mrs. Cranston's (I wasn't married yet) and took a country road toward Waller Creek. This spring-fed stream ran four miles south of town, flowing through pin-oak and blackjack trees that were shielded a hundred yards on both sides from man and civilization by dense yaupon thickets. It's a good place to be alone.

At the bridge I turned into the woods and wandered down the creek maybe three-quarters of a mile, claiming to be thinking but mainly deploring my economic situation, when suddenly I heard a loud, flopping splash in the water ahead. I froze, waited a few seconds, let my eyes adjust, and peered through the shadows into a sunlit pool. In the shallows not ten feet away was an enormous turtle, the biggest I've ever seen, about the size of a number 2 washtub, gnarled and weather-beaten as Captain Ahab and as ancient-looking as Methuselah. Hearing me coming, he had lunged off the bank into a deep pool, swum over to shallow water, and was standing warily on a gravel bar. I guess a turtle can stand warily. I don't know. This story is about one particular turtle, not turtles in general.

I watched him for fifteen or twenty minutes, studying the creek, and figured he was making his home in a cave at the water's edge on the north bank of the pool. He looked as out of place in that little stream as a guided-missile launch pad on a Quaker Church lawn, although I guess ways could be found to make that seem normal and blessed so long as it was for Christianizing purposes. Ex-Commander-in-Chief Nixon, you know, is a Quaker.

The turtle would make a good story, I figured, particularly if I could get a picture of him—the exclusive kind I was trying to make the *Gazette* known for—but I couldn't see any mad rush to subscribe just because I'd stumbled on a big turtle, even though congressmen have been elected on lesser grounds.

Then I got to thinking some more, long and hard and carefully, and a broad grin spread over my face; it was another one of those ideas that flashes into your mind ready-formed, and you almost bust out laughing. Made me feel like Debbs Craig when he thought up his private post office.

I walked hurriedly back to town, went to my office, got what money there was in the safe, and left a note for Clyde, my printer, telling him I'd be out of town the next day and to look after things. Then I went by Buck Carson's hardware store, bought thirty feet of light chain, rented a car from the Ford dealer, and drove back to Waller Creek. Buck wanted to know what in the world I wanted with all that chain and I told him it was to hold a man wanting to buy a load of cedar posts and he said to get the hell out of there. (This'll make sense later on.)

By nightfall I had one end of the chain tied to the left hind leg of that turtle and the other end to a sycamore tree near the edge of the pool. He, or maybe she, I don't know—I told you this wasn't a sex book—didn't like it and made a big commotion at first, lunging this way and that, nearly yanking his leg off, turning and snapping at the chain; but like most of us, he gradually recognized—that is to say, rationalized—his limitations and settled down to his sphere. For all I know he decided he was there to keep the tree from moving off and his life was not without purpose.

I drove back to town feeling like I was in on an international intrigue, packed a bag, and was gone for forty-eight hours.

Next week, splashed on the front page of the *Gazette*, waš this story, set two-columns wide:

190–YEAR–OLD TURTLE TRAVELS
2000 MILES TO GET TO OAT HILL

A 190-year-old turtle, believed to have traveled from Cartright, Mississippi, to Oat Hill, Texas, a distance of 2000 miles or more—figuring the roundabout paths it had to take along winding creeks and rivers—has been found on a creek in Altha County near Oat Hill.

The turtle, about the size of a No. 2 washtub and the largest by far ever seen in this part of Texas, was discovered recently by the editor of the Oat Hill Gazette.

On its back, in plainly readable letters, is carved this: John Temple, Cartright, Miss., 1860.

It was this information which leads to the notion the turtle once lived in Mississippi, but how it traveled the 2,000 circuitous miles from Cartright to near Oat Hill, by what devious streams and by how much sore-footed walking at a turtle's pace the mammoth creature made it all the way to a welcome pool on a creek in Altha County, are questions that amaze the imagination and are hard to answer.

The Gazette editor, however, vouches for the fact he saw the turtle and read the carvings on its ponderous shell.

That's all the story said, but it was exactly enough. If I could have figured out a foolproof way to establish world peace and get China to vote Republican, it wouldn't have attracted a tenth as much interest in Oat Hill. It set the whole county buzzing, carried mostly by word of mouth, since 301 subscriptions don't go far. I guess at least two dozen people stopped me on the street the day the paper came out and demanded more information.

"Let's go see it," Horace Burke said as soon as he got off from the Farmers State, along with fifteen or twenty others, but I put them off. "Got too much work to do, maybe later."

"Well, we'll go see it ourselves. Where is it?"

I said no, it would take a lot of hunting to find it on your own. Besides, I wanted to be there to record their reactions. "Maybe next week. It can't go far, it's too big." So was the tree it was tied to.

Next week, for the first time since I'd founded the *Gazette*, Editor Clayton Martin of the old established *Oat Hill News* got around to mentioning my paper in his. Here's what he said in his front-page personal column, which he called "It Seems to Me":

Quite a bit of excitement has been created by our esteemed contemporary, the Gazette, by its claim that its editor, and he alone, discovered a rather large turtle on a "creek in Altha County" with carvings on its back indicating it came from some other state.

The story was well put together by young Editor Harold Smith and we're wondering if the "turtle" may have come from the same source. At any rate, reflecting the sentiment of a lot of people, all we have to say is, where's the turtle?

"Well, Harold," my most loyal supporters could only manage, "where *is* the turtle? You ought to bring it in, if there is one."

This was bad on my consensus. The ballooning excitement over my turtle story suddenly nose-dived, and while interest in the *Gazette* held up, it wasn't the kind of interest that seemed good for the paper.

Others hooted.

"Hey, Harold, found any giraffes around here lately? Any carving on their backs?"

"Harold, come on down to the Blue Bonnet, they're serving turtle soup. They give you a bowl of milk and you have to imagine there's a turtle in it."

Next week in the *Gazette* I stuck by my guns: "There is a mammoth turtle on a creek in Altha County, it does have some ancient-looking carving on its ancient back, and the *Gazette* next week will publish a picture of it."

That held them off temporarily, putting the thing back in suspense, and I wasn't altogether losing, as thirty-eight subscriptions had come in Saturday afternoon from farmers in town to do their shopping and visiting.

"All I have to say is," a farmer declared as he paid his $1.50, "there'd better be a picture of that turtle in next week's paper."

"When the *Gazette* makes a statement as positive as this turtle declaration, it stands back of its word," I told him, self-consciously squaring my shoulders. I always have felt a little foolish pretending the *Gazette* could make a statement when everybody knows it's just me, but the *New York Times* and the *Dallas News* do it all the time and I guess folklore has its place. "And you tell all your friends if there's not the damnedest picture of the biggest turtle you ever saw in next week's paper I'll refund their subscription money and add a dollar to boot."

Running three columns wide and about eight inches deep in the *Gazette* Thursday was a picture of that turtle, big enough to make your eyes pop. The picture was taken from above and plainly visible on its back was:

JOHN TEMPLE

CARTRIGHT, MISS.

1860

Underneath, this caption ran: "Pictures talk louder than words. Here's that turtle we found on a creek in Altha County."

That's all I wrote, although on the editorial page I had a long article on the habits of turtles excerpted from an encyclopedia, a speculative discussion on how far they could wander, and an estimate of how long it would take one, traveling at about three hundred yards a day, most of the way upstream, to get from Cartright, Mississippi, to Oat Hill, Texas. Also, I had some interviews with various citizens willing to talk about various turtles in their lives, having found, the same as the Associated Press and the television networks, that there's no subject you can't find some people willing to talk about if their name is going to be in the paper or their face on the TV screen. It was a first-rate journalistic job, if I do say so myself, like the *New York Times* covering a flight of the astronauts or the burning of a university, and from the time the paper came out Thursday to closing time Saturday afternoon, 183 new subscriptions came in.

Then Editor Martin kicked the pendulum in the other direction. He wrote:

We noticed the picture of a turtle in the Gazette last week and it was a good picture, a very nice looking turtle, unmistakably a turtle, and there was carving on its back.

The News would like to point out though that there are lots of big turtles in the world, and lots of cameras, and also lots of pocketknives capable of carving on said turtles' backs.

The Gazette's turtle picture merely shows a turtle. We don't deny it, it's clearly a turtle. But we couldn't see a thing about it that indicated it was photographed on any creek in good old Altha County.

We have just one question, which we hope isn't embarrassing: WHERE'S THE TURTLE, EDITOR SMITH?

Human nature is unstable. People are wishy-washy. Mussolini, hanging upside down, discovered that. So did Khrushchev. Lyndon Johnson and Richard Nixon, too. Nearly everybody was on my side last week; this week they were beginning to feel like they'd been hoaxed, thanks to Editor Martin. Apparently there is such a thing as the power of the press, certainly in Oat Hill, and probably in Dallas.

"Say," I overheard one man telling a cluster of men standing in front of the Blue Bonnet, "you know ole Editor Martin has something there. He may be right. Nothing about that picture showed it was taken around here." Instead of hushing up when I drew closer they poured it on all the harder.

"Smith, what're you trying to pull?"

"I don't go for that kind of stuff."

I didn't argue with them, just smiled weakly and kept moving. Never argue with a man who thinks he's right. If followed consistently, this rule would eliminate most arguments.

As I passed Burt Johnson's grocery store, he hailed me from inside.

"Harold, what about this?" He pointed to Editor Martin's article in a copy of the *News* spread out on his desk. When a prospective advertiser talks, I stand at attention the same as a candidate for governor of Texas does before an oil tycoon, or N.B.C. or C.B.S. before a patent-medicine firm. I probably shouldn't say this but, when you get right down to it, I mean if you'll examine who's paying for their programs, David Brinkley and Walter Cronkite, after all, are probably the country's two best known patent-medicine salesmen.

"Yeah, what're you trying to pull?" Bob Griffin, the lumberman, had just walked in. "Where's the turtle? We're your friends. We don't like the way things look. What you got against letting somebody see it? If there is one, you ought to let the people see it and put a stop to all these rumors. You know what people are saying about you?"

"Now just give me time," I insisted, with the unsure-footedness of an economist trying to explain a recession to a tycoon to whom he'd promised a boom. "I'm running a one-horse newspaper and I've got more than one man ought to have to do. But I'll produce that turtle in due time. You know I'm not fool enough to make the whole thing up."

"Hadn't figured you to be, but you'd better get into action," Burt warned.

I walked back to my office, sat down at my typewriter, and wrote the following for Thursday's *Gazette*:

The Gazette's hand has been called. There is a rising tide of demand that we produce a turtle in the flesh, or the shell, you might say. What started out to be only an amusing news article has developed into a raging controversy and we sort of feel like the integrity and accuracy of this paper have been challenged.

When we said we found a washtub-size turtle on a creek in Altha County, we meant it. When we said it has certain carvings on its back, we meant it.

We have been asked to produce the turtle. We will. But instead of showing up in Oat Hill with one, to give rise to more doubts instigated by our esteemed contemporary, the News, we want everybody who's interested to go with us out to the creek where we found it, and see for himself.

If anybody's interested, we will leave the Gazette office promptly at 2 o'clock Saturday afternoon and you're welcome to come along on an expedition to end any and all doubts about this turtle.

This sent excitement boiling over worse than the time the Reverend Horace Barnhart, pastor of the Oat Hill First Baptist Church, mailed in his resignation from Dallas about the same time the choir leader, Miss Elsie Carpenter, left town to see an obstetrician.

By 1 o'clock Saturday afternoon, an hour before expedition time, at least 250 people were milling in front of the *Gazette* office. Anybody who wouldn't think that many people could get so interested in such a local subject, with the world fraught with international crises on every hand, doesn't know enough about human nature. There never was a play on the football field that could out-draw a fist fight in the stands, or an international crisis that could out-pull a love-nest murder in Houston.

I'd hired Carol Lipscomb, a pretty young girl handy with a smile, to sell subscriptions for the day and just before two o'clock she came in and reported she hadn't sold a single one but that at least two hundred people had told her they'd subscribe if we produced that turtle. "Just bring it in and we're ready to buy," was what they were saying. That seemed fair enough.

At two o'clock I came out of my office, grinned a little despite the sinking feeling in the pit of my stomach—what if that turtle had broken loose and disappeared?—and got in a pickup truck I'd borrowed from Martin Standing. The Ford dealer, entering into the spirit of things, had painted on the side of the truck in whitewash: OAT HILL GAZETTE'S TURTLE EXPEDITION. BRING 'EM BACK ALIVE! I honked the horn and pulled out.

A string of cars as long as a funeral procession for a banker with lots of money on loan and a drouth coming on followed me out of town. I might as well admit that I was feeling pretty good and had sense enough to circle the courthouse square, going slow. I estimate there were about 2,500 people in town that day. Three-fourths of them saw the expedition heading out and the rest heard about it.

When we got to Waller Creek I stopped the pickup at the bridge and looked back. Cars were strung out bumper to bumper for a quarter of a mile, car doors slamming, men hurrying forward, excitement mounting as though I'd found a lost gold mine or a missing hydrogen bomb.

It was no trouble to find the turtle; I'd beaten a path to him carrying food around daylight every morning for a month. Leading the crowd up to the pool, I paused while the whole 250 or so had a chance to gather round.

It was a moment comparable to Edison's when the first light bulb came on or Dr. Barnard's when that transplanted heart started beating ("Christ!" he said, "it works!"). Taking hold of the chain tied to the

31

sycamore tree, I pulled slowly and carefully. You could feel the goggle-eyed gaze of the crowd, necks craned, everybody on tiptoe holding his breath.

The chain fed out of the water and the huge turtle broke the surface like a submarine, water sliding off its back, his ancient legs fighting to stay in the pool and his gnarled head alternately coming out and going back under his enormous shell.

As I got him on the bank an involuntary shout went up.

"Look! Look at that thing!"

"It's a turtle all right!"

"Biggest damned thing I ever saw!"

"My God, look at it!"

"Harold wasn't lying!"

"Where's the carving?"

"Yeah, let's see the carving!"

Sure enough, naturally, carved on its back, in letters still plainly visible, was:

JOHN TEMPLE

CARTRIGHT, MISS.

1860

"By gosh, he's right!" Burt Johnson yelled. "It says just what he said it said!"

Excitement spread through the crowd like the news that the astronauts had landed on the moon. Willing hands spread out a tarpaulin I'd brought along and gently caught up the four corners with the beast inside.

"Let's take him back to town," Burt said, as though it was his idea. "This'll prove it! Two thousand miles for one turtle. Must be a world record. All the way from Mississippi! This'll put Oat Hill on the map!" Oat Hill was already on the map. I had looked it up when I was hunting for a place to start a paper.

If going out was exciting, coming in was a hundred times better. The men held their cars back till I got in front and let down a cloth sign on both sides of the pickup! HERE'S THE TURTLE! SUBSCRIBE TO THE GAZETTE.

As we hit town every horn in the parade blasted out and I thought it would be all right to circle the square a couple of times again before pulling up in front of the *Gazette* office.

I crawled out, probably smirking a little, and supervised the unloading, although I wasn't letting anything distract me from the main business at hand. Having already caught the eye of Carol Lipscomb, I gave her the high sign, watched her hit the crowd with receipt book in hand, and saw the subscriptions rolling in.

I tied the turtle to a telephone pole in front of the office, got two boys to stand guard, and backed off. I can tell you, there wasn't much business being done in Oat Hill stores for the next hour or so. Everybody tried to rush that turtle all at once. It was almost a mob until City Marshal Dick Plemons and Sheriff Rod Chanley organized things. They got a line formed up the street and around the next side of the square, and people started filing by. I watched closely when Editor Martin went by, poker-faced.

The excitement lasted pretty well throughout the afternoon and around five-thirty Carol came in looking like she'd been clerking in a bargain basement or fighting off a college boy on a date or the police in the president's office, but she was smiling big. She was working on a commission.

"Guess how many?" she chortled.

"Afraid to say. You guess how many came in over the counter in here."

"I'll tell mine first: 411!"

"Four hundred and . . . incredible. That's wonderful! Ninety-four came in over the counter. That's a total for the day of, let's see, 505."

I locked the money up in the safe, wrote a check for Carol's commission, and walked back into the printing plant to be alone with my thoughts, feeling like a man who had just written a best seller. Never have cold machines looked so entrancing. I felt like shaking hands with the Linotype machine, standing there with one arm held up to its head, elbow bent—that's the way the contraption always struck me. The flatbed press was poised with the round sides of its big cylinder ready to take the sheets of paper in its grippers and roll out next week's *Gazette*—not 301 but more than 1100, a hundred more than I'd ever expected or needed. The *Gazette*, or more specifically, I, Harold Smith, was on the way.

The trouble with Editor Clayton Martin was that he was human, and his human instinct for self-preservation was now aroused. It's a trait handed down by our ancestors. I was no longer an upstart, a nuisance; I was a threat to a life's work. A weekly newspaper's worth isn't calculated in printing equipment; most of its assets are intangible, like the value of being Senate majority leader when television emerges and coming up with the only station permit in the state capital, or of being a friend of the governor when you need a lawsuit stopped. When you or your friend go out of office, those intangibles go too. A weekly newspaper is just the shadow of its editor, plus the habits of his readers. Let something happen to him or the town's reading habits and the creditors have just a few pieces of printing machinery to haggle over. The *Saturday Evening Post*, for example, didn't go out of business because it didn't have enough printing presses.

Therefore, I wasn't surprised or unprepared but only a little apprehensive when the next week's *Oat Hill News* implied in strong words that I was hoaxing the public and that in the long run my type of journalism wouldn't be good for the community. Here's what Editor Martin wrote:

That was quite a show the Gazette editor put on for a gullible public Saturday, pretty well thought out, pretty well planned down to to the last "spontaneous" item. We hope the people got their money's worth.

We'd like to point out, though, as we've been pointing out all along, that while it's true the Gazette editor did produce a big turtle which was chained to a tree on Waller Creek, and it's true it did have carving on its back, it's also true that turtles bigger than that can be imported to Oat Hill and planted on Waller Creek, and any boy who knows his alphabet can carve on its back. He can also look up a likely sounding town in some distant state, say Mississippi, although Oregon would have been farther away, and carve some fictitious name on it and slap on a date and, if he plays it right, sell a lot of newspapers.

We're not saying anything for sure but, if you ask us, the turtle and the turtle story both have an odor.

Well, it's still odd how people can be swayed back and forth, although it shouldn't surprise you; it has been so since history began. I soon detected a sort of morning-after attitude among the people around the square. What had been a fine, enjoyable, uproarious time last Saturday had turned sour by Saturday of the next week. People don't mind being hoaxed—most of us are, in one way or another, from start to finish—but we hate like hell to have it pointed out to us, especially in public. Don't ever try to make a fool of a man in public, unless he's running against you for President.

"Now, Harold," Burt Johnson counseled, and I listened hard because he was now running a half-page grocery ad in the *Gazette* every week, "it's true you produced a turtle, and it's true there's carving on its back indicating it might have come from some place in Mississippi, but what we want to know is, are you pulling our leg?"

It was a question hard to answer. It took a lot of pleasure out of those eleven hundred subscriptions, but not enough to give anybody his money back.

"Look, Burt," I said, choosing my words carefully like a secretary of state answering a delicate foreign affairs question on national television, when he knows he's not going to give a straight answer, "look at it this way. I've backed up everything I've claimed so far in this thing, haven't I?"

He had to admit I had.

"Well, Burt, why not just trust me?" A secretary of state couldn't have asked for less.

Burt said all right. He admitted I was getting out a pretty good newspaper, in fact a jam-up newspaper; his ad was getting results. There was a lot more to read in it than this turtle business. I really reported the news of the town and county like a little *New York Times*, and the people were reading it. But I could see one good hoax caught up with and exposed would tinge everything else in the paper, and I needed every subscription renewed a year from now. Small-towners like to see their name in the paper, same as the President of the United

States and all fifty governors, and weeklies would disappear if they didn't, but they don't care for having their names handled in print by a smart-alec. Neither does the President. Governors aren't quite so particular.

Moreover, Editor Martin wasn't in his dotage. He still had a feel for things, and he sensed the change in attitude, too. His next week's column didn't help me at all:

Another week has gone by and the Gazette has been strangely silent on the turtle business.

You get the impression the Gazette would like to let the matter drop. We believe we understand why, and we freely admit to a certain amount of sympathy for the young editor. Once when we were a boy we pulled a prank that didn't come off all the way and people couldn't forget the thing fast enough to suit us.

But the people in Altha County aren't quite ready to forget and, just to put this thing in the light it belongs in, we're going to ask Editor Smith right here in this public place a few questions.

Editor Smith, DID YOU CARVE THAT NAME AND DATE ON THAT TURTLE'S BACK?

Editor Smith, ISN'T THAT NAME A WHOLLY FICTITIOUS ONE? DIDN'T YOU JUST MAKE IT UP TO HELP ALONG WHAT YOU THOUGHT WAS A GOOD STORY?

It seems to The News editor the least Editor Smith can do is answer these questions next week.

Those were powerful, searching questions. They stimulated more interest in Editor Martin's paper than anything he'd written in years and, while I thought he ought to be a little grateful, he figured he smelled a fox and was riding for all it was worth.

I knew there would be lots of interest, too, in what I had to say and, while I didn't think I had anything to worry about, a man finally runs out of cards. And when he gets down to the last one he's got to win or lose the pot. On the other hand, I'd seen my hole card, though I looked again to make sure. I decided to draw this one out as long as I could. I had to take my time about turning up the last card; I wanted that poker game to end for good. In fact, I told myself if I got through this game ahead I wouldn't play any more.

Monday afternoon, when things quieted down at the office after

Clyde and the bookkeeper had left, I fed Ole Methuselah—that's what I'd named the turtle, although I was prepared to change it to Judas if things didn't work out right—and stood staring at his back, thinking. I kept him or her—I said I don't know any more about turtles than you do—in a metal tank in the office near the front window. Occasionally people came in to look at him, particularly to examine the carving carefully. I had no idea how long he would last in such surroundings but I needed him for a while longer.

I went to my typewriter and wrote:

The Gazette editor knows there is considerable pressure being built up for some answers about our turtle, the pressure pump being handled pretty ably by the editor of the News and, while we are entirely unabashed in the face of the questions, we would like for our readers to give us a little more time for the answers, as we want them to be unarguable.

All we say at the moment is bide your time, suspend your judgment, and the answers will be forthcoming.

It wasn't much a person could chew on. I couldn't say Burt, for example, was reassured, and what Editor Martin had to say next didn't help Burt's confidence:

We notice, instead of answers, a weak plea for more time in last week's Gazette. Take all the time you want, Editor Smith.

But remember there are a lot of people waiting. Those are simple questions to answer, though maybe not too comfortable to answer and then substantiate, and while we can't understand why it takes so long to say yes or no, it's a free country. The News will be around waiting, and prodding. We won't let the matter drop.

Meanwhile, please pass the soup—chicken noodle soup, please; turtle soup has lost its flavor.

Next week I decided on a step that was bold for me but which looked weak and cowardly to nearly everybody else. I didn't say anything. Not a single mention of the turtle in the paper.

I could feel the shock of the people when I went out on the street the day the paper came out.

"What's the matter, Harold?" Burt collared me in the post office. "Ole Man Martin's making you look like two cents. You're gonna have to come up with an answer or a lot of people are gonna want their money back.''

''You'll just have to trust me, Burt.'' I said without smiling and got my mail and walked out. I could hear murmurings about me, guarded, under-the-breath remarks, back-of-the-hand remarks, sneering and distrustful.

I blew the breath out of my cheeks, came back to my office, and sat down at my typewriter. This one had to be a knockout or I was a goner. That week's paper carried just a brief turtle remark.

Once more we'll have to ask your patience. The News no doubt this week will be chomping at the bit for some answers, and not for the benefit of the Gazette.

But for the benefit of our more than 1100 subscribers, which incidentally is the largest circulation of any paper in Altha County, we will say that week after next the Gazette will publish a full and, we trust, satisfying answer to the sniping questions propounded by the News.

As I'd figured, the *News* that same week had another demand for answers, and the following week Editor Martin, feeling he had me on the run and sensing victory, came right out and said:

The Gazette promises a full answer next week. We look forward to it with keen interest.

In fact, we advise all our readers who have been with us so faithfully over the years to buy a copy of next week's Gazette. We want everybody in Altha County to see whether Editor Smith can pull himself out of the hole he has, from youthful inexperience, to put it generously, crawled into. The News right freely urges you to read next week's Gazette.

This was delightful. I guess it was the first time in history an editor advertised his competitor's paper free of charge in such urgent, compelling words. It went far beyond my wildest expectations. Somebody was being led to the slaughter, and I didn't figure it was me. I was sort of looking down Editor Martin's throat. At least I figured I was.

I didn't know what the saturation point in subscriptions was in Oat Hill and Altha County—eleven hundred was enough but more would be even better—so the week before the promised full answer I ran a two-column ad on the front page and printed enough extra copies to blanket the county. Here's what it said:

TAKE A DARE!

Was the celebrated turtle story a hoax? Can the Gazette prove it's authentic?

Tell you what we'll do: In next week's issue we'll prove it beyond any doubt. This week a lot of non-subscribers are getting a free copy of the Gazette through the mail. Next week you won't get a free copy, but we're going to print up a lot of extra copies and have them on hand in the Gazette office for non-subscribers.

Come by and buy a copy any time after 3 p.m. Thursday. Then read it. If you're convinced, then why not subscribe? But don't subscribe until you're convinced the turtle story is no hoax.

THE OAT HILL GAZETTE
Harold Smith, Editor

The following Thursday morning we locked the front door of the *Gazette* office, put up a sign saying we'd open promptly at three P.M. with plenty of copies of the paper available at five cents each, and went to press.

The headline bannered across the top of the front page read: THIS OUGHT TO PROVE IT! And here's the story that followed:

Did that celebrated turtle with the carving on its back travel the 2000 miles all the way from Mississippi to Oat Hill?

Naturally, there's no way of proving it absolutely and positively; he didn't have a keeper following him step by slow step every inch of the way for no telling how many years it took to make the tortuous journey up one stream and down another to that welcome pool on Waller Creek in Altha County. But if there was such a person as John Temple and he did live in Cartright, Mississippi, in 1860, wouldn't that be pretty overwhelming evidence that our poor turtle need no longer hide its face under its shell? And also that the editor of the Gazette has no reason for crawling under with him?

Well, we got to wondering. You suppose there had been a John Temple living in Cartright those many years ago? We decided to find out.

We wrote the editor of the Cartright Sun at Cartright, Mississippi, a man we've never met, and asked him if anybody by the name of John Temple had ever lived there, and if so when.

Well, according to Editor Joel T. Minor of the Cartright Sun, many older citizens there recall John Temple, a man who liked to fish and hunt. When

39

some said he died before 1860 and others said after 1860, the Cartright editor went out to the Cartright Cemetery and there found a tombstone bearing the inscription: "John Temple, Born 1801, Died 1861. A Good Man Has Gone To His Rest."

Obviously, if he did the carving, he did it the year before he died, 1860, as the turtle's back testifies.

But as further proof, we asked the Cartright editor to secure at our expense a picture of the tombstone, and here it is.

Well, of course, that did it. You might say the skeptics, especially Editor Martin, were silent before the tombstone.

There just wasn't any answer to evidence like that, and it was with considerable satisfaction that I saw 416 more new subscriptions come in before the week was out, pushing the total now up well past 1500, which was 500 more than the *News* had. The only thing I didn't feel good about was the apology Editor Martin published in his paper next week.

And there was a feeling beyond satisfaction when I came to work Monday morning and discovered vandals had broken into the *Gazette* office and made off with $4.75 out of a cigar box we kept under the counter for making change, and Methuselah, the turtle. The feeling came not from the loss of the $4.75 but from being free of the turtle. I was as relieved as a gangster when the only eye-witness to his act of murder dies of a heart attack the day before the trial.

I dutifully mourned his loss in that week's *Gazette* and, with my fingers crossed, called on the sheriff to track down the thieves, suggesting that in stealing Methuselah they had taken something of the *Gazette* itself. They had indeed, but it was a wart I was glad to be cured of.

Time has fled and I might as well say here, in a sort of psychological catharsis, that while I did find that turtle on Waller Creek, and there was a tombstone in the Cartright, Mississippi cemetery, it was I who telescoped the two facts together. I had done this by getting in a rented car that daring Thursday evening months ago and driving all night as hard as I could to get to Mississippi, then picking out a cemetery in a town big enough to have a newspaper, and carefully noting the inscription on a likely looking tombstone: JOHN TEMPLE, BORN 1801. DIED 1861. I had done the rest with my pocketknife.

You might say what I did was wrong, and you might be right. But I didn't cut deep enough into the shell to hurt the turtle.

People don't mind being out-thought if you out-think them far enough and don't get caught. I took my escape as a great moral lesson, bearing witness to Abe Lincoln's faith in the solid idea that you can fool all the people some of time, but stop right there. Once I had got respectability, which in my case was fifteen hundred paid subscriptions, I didn't push my luck any farther. Rather, I settled down to producing the best weekly newspaper my energies and talents would allow and, if I do say so myself, Oat Hill benefited by it.

And Editor Martin? His paper kept going satisfactorily, too, and we're friends. Just last week I had my Linotype operator set all his type for him when his operator got sick. I believe he'd do the same for me.

When it comes to ethics there are very few eligible first-stone-throwers, although you ought to be prepared to dodge the rocks from hypocrites. How many nations have been built on pure and undefiled ethics? The Roman Empire? Greece? The British Empire? Russia? And where would America be today if we had respected the Indians' property rights?

I take the optimistic view of human nature—I think that while it's true there's a lot of bad in the worst of us, still there's a little bit of good in the best of us.

5

A Fast Buck

By this time some readers will be saying that what I did with that turtle was unethical—maybe even what I did to Congressman Nat Caxton was, or what Debbs Craig did to Postmaster Albert Barton or what happened to an entire courthouse square, which will come out later on. But I can't help that.

Ethics in a world that has been at war most of the time for several thousand years, or between two genocidal tribes of ants, is a maneuverable word, like fast. You know, you can *run fast* and you can be *tied fast*. It all depends on which lawyer you've hired. It's like reconciling the atomic bomb drop with Baptist theology. Harry Truman had no trouble with it and I like Harry Truman, if not the bomb, although, if bombs are going to exist among nations, I'm glad we've got some.

All I know is that being alive is fun. Planting a garden is fun, and no doubt painting the ceiling of the Sistine Chapel was. Yet any of these, if done long enough, will give you a backache. Enjoyment— physical, mental, and spiritual—is the only possible half answer I can find to the mainly unanswerable bafflement of being born and coming to self-consciousness on a globe whirling in a boundless universe. And it is inabsolute. What I mean is, when one hundred men are through living, it can never be determined which one had the most fun and therefore was the most fulfilled; it's not computerable.

Novelists and playwrights amuse me. They take life and themselves with unmerciful seriousness. They exhaust themselves examining the oddballs and off-shoots and the psychologically hung-up and claim they're reporting life. And they are, just as a biologist is reporting on biology when he reports only on two-headed babies.

These literati swallow whole Thoreau's notion that the vast majority of men lead lives of quiet desperation, when a more accurate observation is that the small minority of men lead lives of frantic desperation.

I can't say about other places but the average man in my town of Oat Hill is not desperate, any more than the average cow on my ranch is desperate, or the average member of any other species, excusing maybe whooping cranes and aging members of the Politburo.

If he isn't in the poverty class which, as inexcusable as it is, is still a small minority, at least in the United States, he finds life is fun and he lives zestfully, unbothered by hidden fears and psychological guilt, and is mostly intrigued with being alive.

There's the key. When you're interested in what you're doing—whether it's running a country newspaper or a grocery store or practicing psychiatry or writing a novel—if it's not criminal, you're a successful human animal, whether your name is a household word throughout the land or unknown thirty miles away.

Moreover, the size of your enterprise is no gauge. Running a store successfully in Oat Hill is as much fun as running Macy's in New York, and I don't see how editing the *Times* up there could be any more fun than editing the *Gazette* down here. (I've seen the editors of the *New York Times* in earnest discussions on television, and they all look like men who could be fired. I can't be.) I believe you can enjoy life as much here as there, that walking four miles through the woods around Oat Hill is as much fun as walking through the woods of New Hampshire or the Black Forest of Germany; that the ground in front of the *Oat Hill Gazette* is just as ancient as the streets of Jerusalem; that the fun of writing has to be in the writing and the knowledge that it'll be read and paid for, not in the number who'll read it. Whether you're writing for five thousand or five million readers amounts only to whether you're writing for one one-millionth or one one-hundred-thousandth of the three and a half billion people alive on earth. At the top of the all-time best-seller list, you're reaching only an infinitesimally small fraction of the species. Whatever you write, there are millions more people who'll never hear of it than those who do.

I like a quiet joke, the kind you pull for your own private amusement to resist the occasional gloom of the awfulness of endless space, which you can't imagine extending out forever or coming to a stop either. Try it for five seconds, but no longer. It's a good way to pop your skull.

While it has never happened, if I were asked by a pollster how I'm going to vote in a coming election, I'd tell him wrong, just for the satisfaction of picturing my opinion turning up as an incorrect statistic. Sure it's a small pleasure but, if you check back, you'll find living consists of innumerable small pleasures. All the big pleasures exist chiefly, if not totally, in fiction. I return postage-paid postcards unsigned and get a good feeling imagining what goes on in the office in the far-off city when the card returns there, figuring anticipation is two-thirds of the fun of any enterprise, including maybe sex, and certainly most marriages. The way I look at it is, if I caused the outfit some anticipatory pleasure, what wrong did I do and who cares anyway?

Sometimes I use a refined method. Instead of returning a card unsigned I scratch an absolutely illegible signature on it and give an illegible address. This works fine on insurance promotion schemes, termite control firms, encyclopedia publishers, famous writers' schools, and other such outfits wanting to send a salesman around. If it's a perfectly harmless deal, like a correspondence course on how to become a beauty-shop operator, it's all right to print in the name of the town's leading society woman. Mrs. Clarence Millington, president of the Oat Hill Reading Club, is always wondering why some company would think she'd like to become a beauty operator.

One time I got mad at the Bell Telephone Company and for a period there every month when I paid my bill, say it was for $14.28, I'd make my check for $14.29 and speculate on how much trouble it was for the big corporation to carry the penny balance over to my next bill.

One time when I was still in college I was sitting on a bench with a friend in a park in Austin eating a bag of peanuts and watching the squirrels, so tame they'd come up and eat out of your hand. I ate all my peanuts, put the shells back in the bag and held it out. A squirrel raced over, rummaged through it, and backed off in chagrin when it found nothing but empty husks. I laughed and, because my friend was outraged, I explained all I was doing was firming up the animal's character, teaching it one of the truths of the universe. How to handle a disappointment is one of the first lessons to learn if you want to live a humorously enjoyable life. This is a fine universe but it has some flaws that squirrel and the rest of us need to face up to.

I wouldn't beat anybody out of a dollar, even if he had no way of catching up with me, and that's the true test of honesty. I don't think I would, unless I were hungry, which I've never been in the Mid-East sense of the word. Lots of times ethics is a luxury practiced by the rich after they've become rich, which I guess you could argue is better than never. I have a notion one cave man decided it would not be ethical to hit another man with his club only after he had gotten through with his slugging and had all the food and wood he needed for the winter stored up in his own cave.

Think of the many civilized minds that have made genuine contributions to mankind, made possible mainly by an uncivilized grab for wealth, either by their forebears or their rulers. In the field of ethics people aren't purebreds, they're crossbreeds. A man whose life is an open book makes mighty dull reading. A lot of effective, useful politicians arrived at their plateaus of usefulness by routes that called for something other than absolute honesty and fair play every step of the way. Going through life without ever having hurt a fly sounds to me impossible, not to say unsanitary. The shortest distance to usefulness sometimes is a wavy line. Some irresponsible ones even claim a crooked line was the shortest distance between the Pedernales and the Potomac. Probably Republicans. Personally, I thought L.B.J. was a pretty good President. Anybody who doesn't suit the intellectuals is bound to have something on the ball.

Take newspaper ethics. I know some newspapers claim they publish all the news, and some say they print all the news that's fit to print, but none of them is one hundred percent honest about it. No paper prints *all* the news. Most news never gets past the oral stage and a lot never even reaches that stage, to the relief of the men and women thereby remaining unshot. If there ever was any news unfit to print, it must have been what happened in Hitler's unspeakable gas chambers, but what paper omitted it?

On the *Gazette*, my policy is to publish all the news it takes to go around the ads, probably the same policy most metropolitan papers use. I've noticed, invariably, that on the days ads are scarce, news is too. You can't make me believe there's eight times as much news in the world on Saturday, reflected in fat Sunday issues, as there is on Sunday reflected in thin Monday issues.

I've never had a fixed, inflexible policy on news. It's like trying to have a rigid policy for raising two different kids or laying out your clothes today for day after tomorrow's weather. Adaptability is what keeps newspapers and species alive. Ask the snow rabbit that hypocritically turns from white to brown when the stuff melts in the spring. I was squirrel hunting with a friend one time when a squirrel in a nearby tree kept chattering and barking but stayed hidden behind a limb. "Come out and fight like a man," my friend said. "Oh, no," I said, "come out and fight like a squirrel. If he fights like a man, he'll start shooting at us."

A lot of news has been left out of my paper because I never heard about it (same as the Associated Press), or didn't have time to write it or the space to put it in; other news has been left out because I decided to omit it. Here's a sample:

One day my friend Buck Carson was standing in front of his hardware store on the east side of the courthouse square in Oat Hill wishing a customer would show up.

A beat-up bobtailed Chevrolet truck with a load of cedar posts pulled in at the curb. A young cedar-brake woodchopper from Central Texas wearing dirty overalls, needing a haircut, his shoe laces broken, and his greasy hat coming down on his ears, unwired the door handle, got out, looked his load of posts over, kicked a front tire, and walked over to Buck.

"Could I interest you in a load of posts, Mr. Carson?"

"Naw, don't believe so," Buck said.

"Sell you this load for thirty cents apiece. Good mountain cedar. Six-inch tops. Got about two hundred on the truck. Thirty cents is a mighty close price."

"Nope. Not interested."

"Well, if you change your mind, I'll be in town till around midafternoon." He got into his truck and drove off and Buck went back inside.

Ten minutes later a man in cowboy boots and a big hat walked in, letting the screen door slam behind him.

"What can I do for you?" Buck asked, laying aside his flyswatter and coming forward. Buck hated flies and Democrats.

"Got some fencing to do. Need about twenty rolls of bobwire and some posts."

"I got the wire, but I don't have any posts on hand right now."

"One won't do me no good without the other."

"How many posts you need?"

"Oh, a couple of hundred, at least."

"What size?"

"Six-footers. Five or six-inch tops. You know where I can get some?"

"I might. How much you willing to pay for 'em?"

"No more'n I have to."

"Would you pay forty cents?"

"Well, I would if I had to. Know where I can get some?"

"I tell you what," Buck said, "you come back in a couple of hours and I may be able to fix you up."

"Okay, I got a grocery list to fill, be in town a couple of hours. See what you can do." He walked up the street and around to the other side of the courthouse.

Buck went out front and looked both ways up and down the street, squinting in the sunlight. Two hundred posts at a dime profit each is twenty dollars, plus the profit on twenty rolls of wire—not a bad day's work.

Five minutes later he brightened. There was the cedar-brake man in his bobtailed truck driving back onto the square with his load of

47

posts. Buck waved him down and he pulled his truck into the curb and crawled out.

"Say, I changed my mind," Buck said. "What's the least you'll take for those posts?"

"Thirty cents, like I said."

"That's too much, but I believe I'll take 'em. Pull around to the back and unload."

An hour later the woodchopper came in the store, wet from unloading, pocketed his check for sixty dollars, thanked Buck, stepped inside the Farmers State Bank and cashed the check, got in his truck and drove off. Circling around to the other side of the square, where he was shielded by the courthouse, he picked up the man in the cowboy boots and the big hat, his favorite brother-in-law, and drove on back to his home near Belton.

Buck finally worked the posts off, a few at a time, and nobody was hurt, but I couldn't see any point in publishing the story. Never hold a man up to ridicule if you intend to keep doing business with him. Occasionally Buck runs an ad in the *Gazette*.

Now this involves a moral, I guess, but I'll tell you, I like Buck, have for years; yet I have to admit I also like that woodchopper. I like to see a man use his wits. I know it's considered unethical to make a fast buck, unless you make it changing women's dress lengths from season to season or making last year's automobiles obsolete by this year's hood design, but do you know how much work it takes to cut two hundred cedar posts with an ax? And how do I know the woodchooper didn't take that money and buy his kids some clothes so they could go to school? And they may have later gone to college and some day one of them may be a congressman or the governor of this state or a principal of a grammar school.

It all depends on how long ago the fast buck was made. There have been many men whose charitable foundations and genuine public service did a world of good, whose original money came from some fairly fast bucks, and whose descendants lived lives of great usefulness. Don't you think so, Mr. Rockefeller? Mr. Harriman? Teddy?

On the other hand, here's an example of the use of a man's wits I don't go for.

For several months Nellie Stevens had been nagging her husband, Mat, about a small leak in the kitchen roof of their home six miles north of Oat Hill.

Mat climbed up on the roof half a dozen times trying to patch it but with every rain water came trickling into Nell's kitchen.

One day an itinerant repairman came by and Mat grabbed him.

"Can you fix a leaky roof?" he asked.

"Sure I can," the man said. "That's my speciality."

"You guarantee it?"

"Certainly. Show me where it's leaking."

He looked it over and said he'd fix it for twenty-five dollars.

"Go on about your work, I'll go up in the attic and get at it," he said. In an hour he was back down.

"It's fixed," he said.

"Now you guarantee it?" Mat asked.

"If water comes down through that kitchen ceiling the next time it rains, I'll refund your money the next time I'm by here."

Mat paid him. A few days later it rained and not a drop of water came through.

"Well, finally," Nellie said. Mat sighed and said he was glad that problem was licked.

A week later it rained again and water came trickling through the ceiling into the kitchen.

Mat rushed up into the attic to see what had happened.

Under the spot where the water was coming through the roof was a bucket. It had held all the leak from the first rain but was now full and overflowing.

Now this I would call unethical on a personal basis, but on a wider scale it's the way the world solves most of its big problems. In Viet Nam, for example, we've spent a hundred billion dollars on buckets and the leak is still there.

6

The Triumph of Wit

The only man in Oat Hill to whom I ever gave even a glimmer of a hint of the facts of the shady turtle business was John Short, a lumberman and a free enterpriser of the first rank.

I was in Mr. Short's office one day about a year after the shenanigans to pick up an ad for the *Gazette* and he asked me how I was doing.

"Pretty good," I said. "Everything seems to be going fine. I'm out of debt, I own a newspaper that's making a little money, and I'd get you to put me up a new building of my own if I could find a location on the square."

Only there weren't any vacant lots anywhere on the courthouse square in Oat Hill. There weren't any buildings that could be bought, and the matter wasn't pursued. But the idea of owning my own building later caused me to do the oddest thing in my life. It also was the most fun.

"I like your spirit," Mr. Short said. "You don't seem to let people back you down. I like to see a young fellow get ahead; like to see him make a place for himself like you've done here. Country needs more little fellows with backbone enough to take care of themselves. You know, I thought for a while you were going to take a licking on that turtle affair."

"To tell you the truth, I thought so too for a while." But that was as far as I was going.

"Ever tell you how I got started on my own in the lumber business?"

I could tell Mr. Short was fixing to reminisce and I was fixing to listen. I told you I was there to pick up an ad.

"No. I'd like to hear." I eased into a chair and lit a cigarette and leaned back. I guess he talked for an hour and a half and this is the way it went.

John Short came to Texas from a mountainside farm in Tennessee when he was twenty, possessing an eighth-grade education and a headlong desire to make something of himself. For no particular reason he landed in Prairieville, which is twenty miles from Oat Hill in the adjoining county and even then was big enough to have a small daily newspaper.

He got a job as a yard man in Old Man Taylor's lumber yard, unloading lumber when it came in by box car, stacking it in the sheds, loading it out on wagons when it was sold, sweeping out the office, and doing anything else he was told to do.

While John loaded lumber during the day he stayed in his room at night studying bookkeeping. After about a year Mr. Taylor discovered that not only could he keep an accurate set of books, but he also could figure lumber. He could sit down with a pencil and figure up every foot of lumber a house or barn would require, including how many pounds of nails and how many squares of shingles, and when he got through he'd be so close to what the job actually took you could safely base your bid on it. It wasn't long before John was working in the office and, while he gave the office job everything it took, he still had energy left. During his off hours he kept right on thinking about the lumber business and it wasn't long before he was bringing in customers. People seemed to like to deal with John Short. If he said a wagonload of lumber would be delivered at two P.M., it was delivered at two P.M., even if he had to drop his bookkeeping and help load it out himself and finish up his books at night.

Mr. Taylor took notice of this and, when the town of Oat Hill began to grow and he decided to expand with a branch yard there, he figured John Short was the man to manage it. He was right. If ever a man put in all his waking hours selling lumber, learning his customers, separating the good credit risks from the deadbeats and making a lumber yard go, John Short did. It's the same sort of drive that makes junior executives for soap companies out of Harvard graduates.

The Oat Hill branch of the Taylor Lumber Company showed a profit almost from the start. At the end of two years it was doing far more than Mr. Taylor had ever dreamed. One day, in an expansive mood brought on by the rumor that a big lumber-yard chain out of Waco had its eye on John, Old Man Taylor called him into his Prairieville office and told him: "John, you're doing a first-rate job. You're making money for me. I know you're ambitious and I like ambitious young men. Tell you what I'm going to do. You stick with me another year and I'll sell you half interest in the Oat Hill yard. How's that?"

"That's fine, Mr. Taylor. I appreciate it. It's exactly what I want," John said, and went back to Oat Hill and worked harder.

At the end of the year John was ready but the offer seemed to have slipped Mr. Taylor's mind. John waited and fidgeted a month, then went over to Prairieville and brought the matter up.

"Well, I tell you, John." Old Man Taylor cleared his throat. "Uh, things aren't going exactly to suit me here in Prairieville. The lumber business is fine, that's true, but I've had a lot of family expense lately, boy in college, another one getting ready, and my wife may have to have an operation. I know I promised to sell you a half interest, but let's wait a little while on it. I'm going to do it; I said I would and I will, but let's look at it this way. I helped you get a start; you're doing mighty well for a young man. Think what you had when I first gave you a job and let's not rock the boat for the time being. Why don't you go on back and just keep running the yard like you have, I'm mighty pleased with it, and a little later on that half interest will be waiting for you."

Well, John said, all right, he did owe a lot to Mr. Taylor, and he went back to Oat Hill and sold more lumber, for the same salary.

In the meantime John had married and in three and a half years was the father of three boys.

Walking back to work after lunch one day, he got to thinking hard, not about the lumber business but about family business. He and Mrs. Short had been trying to figure out how to cut down on expenses.

He had instituted every type of economy known to man or Republican—in preelection speeches only—and a good many he'd invented on his own. He milked a cow after dark when he got home from work to supply the three boys, got up before daylight and milked again, wore his suits long after they should have been thrown away, cut down on the food bills, turned off the lights, and sat by the flames from the fireplace, but it wouldn't work. He had three boys on hand and another baby on the way. Where in the world could he cut down more to take care of the next one?

As he rounded a corner a sudden thought hit him! There wasn't any way he could cut down on expenses any more. He couldn't economize himself into security. The only salvation for John Short, if he wanted to raise and educate a family, was not to scrimp more but to make more. It was a simple thought, but for him it was a great one.

"Been working on the wrong end of the problem," he told himself, and his resolution increased with every step. By the time he got to the lumber yard he was walking fast.

He did a full afternoon's work at the office but after he got home that night he figured late.

What he did, after a month's calculating, was decide to open up a lumber yard of his own in Oat Hill. First he resigned as manager of the Taylor Lumber Company's branch yard. He didn't leave any door open for bargaining about that half interest, just wrote Mr. Taylor he was resigning but would stay on until he got somebody to take his place, provided he got somebody in thirty days. Old Man Taylor bargained and pleaded, even threatened a little, but John wouldn't budge. At the end of thirty days a new manager arrived and John put on his hat and walked out and opened up his own lumber yard.

That is, if you can call a shirttail full of lumber and a few kegs of nails a lumber yard. But John had two assets: he had the confidence of A.W. Star, who was running the First National Bank in Oat Hill then, and that of the lumber mills. He could get a reasonable amount of lumber on credit and A.W. Star was willing to lend him a reasonable amount of money on his character.

As he had calculated, customers hadn't been buying lumber from him at the Taylor branch yard because the lumber there was better or the nails stronger; they'd been buying lumber service, and John figured he was responsible for the service.

He was right. He began to make his yard go. There were critical times at first. It's no easy job to buy lumber on credit, sell it, get a house built, collect for it, and pay the wholesaler and the bank too, while still feeding a family, but John managed. He was beginning to see daylight, could feel solid footing ahead, and had begun enjoying the fruits of owning his own lumber yard, when lightning struck.

In that week's *Oat Hill News* the Taylor Lumber Company branch yard had a half-page ad announcing a drastic cut in the price of lumber.

Old Man Taylor may have miscalculated how far he could push John Short without bringing him in as a partner and splitting the profits, but he wasn't short of fighting spirit. He, too, believed this was a free country, and what he had decided to do was freeze John out. It's not an unheard-of thing in American business or international power politics. Lots of big businessmen believe in free enterprise and competition only after they have a monopoly in their field. Ask the telephone company. By foregoing his profits in Oat Hill for a while and living on his profits in Prairieville, Mr. Taylor figured he could get along satisfactorily while young John Short, still on a shoestring, went under.

John was thunderstruck. He hadn't foreseen the obvious. Sure, with the Taylor Lumber Company branch selling lumber at cost, the John Short Lumber Yard couldn't last long. You can sell on friendship and service when most things are even but when your price is way out of line friendship and service lose their appeal. There's a saying, that if you want your children to visit you in your old age don't give them their inheritance while you're still alive. Money is thicker than blood. John knew he couldn't sell lumber at cost and survive. He was up the creek, as they say in East Texas. He had four children now and children, like citizens of their government, demand more and more.

Now some men, confronted by a desperate situation, throw up

their hands and holler calf rope, or stick around and mope and pray for a miracle and await the inevitable.

John Short was different. After thinking his problem over for a week, he put up a sign one day announcing he was closed for the afternoon, rented a buggy, and rode the twenty miles over to Prairieville. Tying his horse in front of the *Prairieville Daily Press*, he went in, to emerge thirty minutes later and start back to Oat Hill.

The next afternoon's Prairieville newspaper carried the following quarter-page ad:

BUY YOUR LUMBER IN OAT HILL
The following prices are good at ALL lumber
yards in Oat Hill:
No. 1 shiplap .... $20 per M.
2x4s, No. 1 .... $22 per M.
Siding, B & B .... $28 per M.
Nails .... 2¢ lb.

And there were a lot of other prices, all listed at cost. John used the same prices the Taylor Lumber Company had used in its ad in the *Oat Hill News*.

Well, next morning Old Man Taylor's phone at his Prairieville lumber office was ringing off the wall.

"How come you're selling lumber cheaper at your yard in Oat Hill than you are here?" Cap'n A. F. Perry was the first to ask. He was the biggest contractor in Prairieville. "It's the same kind of lumber, ain't it?"

"What're you trying to do, hold us up here in Prairieville?" Sam Stark wanted to know. He'd just built eight rent houses and was figuring on twelve more in a new addition he'd opened.

You get the drift. Wasn't long before business was booming at the Oat Hill branch of the Taylor Lumber Company, dwindling fast in Prairieville. Folks in Prairieville were driving twenty miles over to Oat Hill, buying lumber by the wagon load at cost, and hauling it back to Prairieville. If they tried to buy any at John's yard, he'd manage to be out of that particular size and assure them they could get it at the Taylor yard.

Lightning was now striking in the other direction. Old Man Taylor was faced with something *he* hadn't foreseen. That wasn't the way he'd figured it at all. He could live without the profits from his Oat Hill yard but not without those from his main Prairieville yard. He'd just got a letter from his boy in college saying he needed more money.

He thought his problem over about a week, then got in his buggy and headed for Oat Hill. You can say this for him, he recognized a tight situation when he was in it. He pulled up in front of John Short's office, went in, and sat down. John was sort of expecting him.

"John," he said right off, "you win. Let's quit making fools of ourselves and see if we can't both make some money in Oat Hill."

John said he sure was willing, and the next day prices of lumber in Oat Hill went back up to normal. As it turned out, both yards survived. John forged ahead considerably, but Oat Hill began to grow some more and both yards dug in. While Old Man Taylor died years ago and his heirs sold his lumber business, there are still two lumber yards here. John is one of the town's most substantial citizens. He's a director in one of the banks, owns a lot of land around here, and sent five boys and two girls though college.

After he got through telling me the story, I smiled and told him I had done considerable thinking ahead myself on that celebrated turtle story before I introduced it to the public. He laughed and said he figured I had.

"By the way," I said, "you want your ad this week to run a full page, don't you?" And he was feeling so good he said yes.

Never let your mind stray very far from your own business.

7

The Oat Hill Electronic
Pure Democracy Machine

The idea is so simple you wonder why it wasn't thought of sooner. But wait a minute. I'm getting ahead of myself again. There was this letter from Congressman Jake Dill that began, "Dear Harold, I am astonished. . . ."

Jake had replaced Nat Caxton in this district after the *Gazette* had brought on Nat's downfall, although I can't say it was an improvement. This probably explains why so many congressmen, once elected, stay elected. Voters yawn and figure the next one will be about like the current one. It's the same instinctive knowledge that keeps many marriages together. The partners know each got about what he or she deserved and a change would just be a lot of trouble for nothing.

"I am astonished to learn that so many people, as you say in your letter of Jan. 4, are opposed to a dam on the Coon River in Altha County," the congressman's letter continued.

"As you know, the U.S. Corps of Army Engineers, after careful and detailed studies, recommended that this dam be built, and it has been endorsed by all the Chambers of Commerce throughout the entire watershed, which takes in part of my district and three other congressional districts. Those civic leaders say this 40-million-dollar project will be an economic boon to that area, bringing in many new people to enjoy fishing and lakeside living.

"I have the petition you sent me signed by 3,114 farmers and ranchers living in the Altha County area that will be flooded by the dam and stating their opposition to its construction. I will give it careful consideration, but I am afraid at this point the project is too far advanced to be stopped. I appreciate your writing me and I will be in touch with you regarding this matter. Your friend, Jake Dill, M.C.''

"Damn it," Jake probably had said as he looked up at his assistant, "why didn't we know there was that much opposition to this thing?" I imagine he then reached for his bottle and poured a drink and said, "We got to keep in better touch with the people back there."

I got to thinking, I guess ole Jake is telling the truth, he really didn't know there was a lot of opposition to that dam, although if he'd read the *Gazette* like Nat Caxton did he'd have known. It's an outright sin, covering up all that good farm land, all those pecan orchards, just so a bunch of drunks can go fishing.

Sure, the Coon River gets on an occasional rise, sometimes a big one like in 1957 when it was two miles wide and washed out every fence for thirty miles but, thunder, we can live with it. As a rancher on the river told me, "I'd a heap rather be flooded occasionally by an act of God than permanently by an act of the Army Engineers."

The more I thought the wider awake I got. This is ridiculous. Imagine in this day and age a congressman having to guess what the voters think. How many times have other congressmen, presidents, state representatives, county judges, and mayors been mistaken about how their constituents feel? What an odd way to have representative government—depending on letters, on local henchmen, on polls, on instinct. Sure, instinct would tell a congressman his district would welcome a 40-million-dollar project paid for by the federal government, but instinct doesn't always work. Instinct should have told the dinosaurs they were getting too big. It should have told the whooping cranes not to fly so low over duck blinds, and it should have told the Indians not to teach the Plymouth Rock settlers how to grow corn and survive to take their land.

Now in the old days a congressman *had* to guess what his constituents thought, ride a train back home once or twice a year and shake hands and confer and listen and hope he heard right. In ancient Athens the Greeks beat that; they would assemble everybody on a

58

greensward and decide an issue with a show of hands, not counting those of the slaves.

A professor at the Massachusetts Institute of Technology was complaining about this some time ago, pointing out that the quality of a traditional town meeting is missing from politics today. "Mass democracy in the hectic environment of the twentieth century tends to lose this quality of democracy precisely because there is no feedback from the voters to the politicians," he said.

Coming from a man teaching at an institute of technology, this is a classic example of not being able to see the forest for the trees.

Twentieth-century America can enjoy the precise quality of a town-hall meeting in its politics if it will use the Oat Hill Electronic Pure Democracy Machine, which I have invented down to the last coil of wire and data-processing components and which I have failed to put into production only because of an obtuse Congress' failure to appropriate a billion dollars.

This is what you get from a Congress trying to run a country by keeping its ear to the ground when two-thirds of the people now live on upper floors.

This machine will tell you instantaneously what 200 million people think on any issue or about any candidate at any time. You are wondering, of course, how it works.

It's simple. The basic element is enough ordinary telephone wire to run to every house and apartment in the United States, strung on the telephone poles already at hand in most cases, plus five or six secondary electronic computers and one mammoth computer. You could have just one computer located in Washington but, by the time you got a wire from every house in the country strung into the capitol, it would certainly be a mess of wires. No, the more practical way is to divide the country into areas; let the Southwest area, for example, feed its wires to Dallas, the Midwest to Kansas City, and so on, and, at voting time, these secondary computers could flash the area results to the mammoth computer in Washington with a loss of no more than a second or two.

I'm not sure I've made myself clear; the simplest truths are sometimes the hardest to grasp, as I proved with my turtle.

What I've set out to do is establish the principle of the traditional town meeting where issues are settled by a show of hands in a nationwide, functioning form of pure democracy for 200 million people, so elections can be decided instantaneously, right out in the open. But I hurry to say that voting on candidates is just one of the incidental uses of the Oat Hill Electronic Pure Democracy Machine, although one of its substantial benefits would be to assure a one hundred percent voter turnout without the services of a single precinct boss or one rung doorbell. There are many other uses.

For instance, when a man is elected to Congress, however democratically pure the voting was, pure democracy is no more certain to result after he gets there than truth is when a man takes an oath to tell it.

One hundred percent democratic representation after the election is what we're aiming at. Congressman Jake Dill was elected fairly democratically, but he didn't represent his constituents in the Coon River dam matter. Under the present unwieldy, guess-as-guess-can system, a congressman can only calculate what the people favor and vote in Washington aye or nay as his antenna tells him, if a lobbyist hasn't gotten to him first. Incidentally, this machine would just about throw lobbyists out of work completely. It would absolutely eliminate this haphazard, static-fraught, loose-wire system.

Let's take an example. Fidel Castro, say, makes a four-hour speech and finally gets around to saying he's tired of being hugged to death by Moscow for less economic aid than he figures he could get elsewhere and now asks us to let Cuba come in as the fifty-first state.

This proposal throws Congress into an uproar, as not a single member had any such plank in his platform during the campaign, for or against, and his constituents never said a word about it. Every congressman is in the dark, and that's the worst place for a congressman to be except for those who'd be worse off if caught in broad daylight.

Therefore, under the present system, they ask the people to express themselves, and are thereupon overwhelmed with letters, telegrams, and telephone calls for and against letting Cuba in. Castro agents in this country systematically inspire thousands of telegrams for it, Russian agents inspire just as many against, both sides round up highly respectable people like college professors, outspoken ministers, hordes of liberals, intellectuals, garden club members, etc. Some un-influenceable people take the time to write, while others stay silent.

This is a strange way to achieve democracy. A mere shouting match. Like a hundred students claiming to tell the college administration what twenty thousand think. Under my system, deciding the issue would be quiet, orderly, effortless, and 100 percent accurate, with not a single congressman risking his job by voting wrong.

The mammoth computer in Washington, told to get an expression from the people on admitting Cuba to statehood, notifies the secondary computers around the country; they in turn alert every household, first with a few bars of the Star Spangled Banner coming out of the loud speaker, which I forgot to tell you the wire leading to your house is connected with, then with a red flashing light. And on the little closed-circuit television screen just above the "yes" and "no" buttons in your home voting booth would appear this question: "Do you favor admitting Cuba as the fifty-first state?" A voice also would keep asking the question for the benefit of the illiterate.

At this point pure electronic democracy takes over. The husband pushes a "yes" or "no" button, his wife pushes her choice, and any other eligible voters domiciled there push theirs. The computer in Dallas, if you live in the Southwest, starts recording with lightning speed as buttons are pushed all over the area and twenty-four hours later (that's how long the polls would be open) flashes its results to Washington. There the national computer digests the area results and announces the grand totals on a tamper-proof screen located just above the speaker's chair in the House of Representatives. Out of respect for tradition, there'd be no screen in the Senate, but a courier equipped with a sixty-second camera would photograph the tally right off the screen and walk over to that body and let the vice president read it aloud.

Right now I can hear somebody saying, "Yeah, but how do you know somebody didn't push his home button too many times? Too easy to rig such an election; beats raiding tombstones for names. Chicago would go wild over it."

61

Having worked on this machine a long time when I should have been working on the *Gazette*, I have the answer to that.

The computer in your area headquarters has been told to memorize on tape exactly the number of votes in your household. If you have two votes in your house and three come winging down the wire, the computer gets indigestion, flashes something sort of like TILT in a marble machine; there's a great clanging of bells and in an instant your name and address appear on a punch card in the caretaker's office. From there on it's between you and the F.B.I.

Incidentally, if you have two votes in your house and no votes reach the computer, it automatically punches your card for a twenty-five-dollar fine, which is automatically recorded with the Internal Revenue Service and added to your income tax. Talk about getting out the vote!

This preposterous issue of statehood for Castro's Cuba is just an example. Actually, the machine would be used for obtaining views on all the grave and perplexing crises that arise daily in a democracy of two hundred million people and keep congressmen unsure about how to vote. Should we increase or decrease foreign aid? Why ask a bunch of congressmen to guess what the people think? Why leave it up to a President who doesn't ask anybody? Why not ask the people themselves? This isn't 1880.

To keep people from having to hang around their home voting booth constantly, it would be simpler to let the crises sort of stack up and settle them only once a month. Half of them wouldn't be around by then anyway.

This machine is entirely within the scientific and budgetary capacity of the United States and I don't see why it isn't used. This idea of letting my congressman guess how I feel on any issue is unfair both to him and to me, and I offer the machine free to the people of my country with no royalties expected, although I would like to be paid for the time it took to think it up.

Women's Liberation

Some people think new ideas, like my voting machine, invariably originate in cities and years later spread out through the boondocks, but that's mostly another example of big-city provincialism.

Take women's liberation. I encountered it years ago in a small college in a small Texas town.

This red-headed, independent-thinking sophomore coed, at a joint YMCA–YWCA meeting on campus one night, said it was ridiculous, if not insulting, for the man to bear all the costs of a date.

"I get as much allowance from home as most of you boys here; why should you pay my way into the picture show?" she asked. "At home on the ranch, nobody helps me onto a horse. I saddle up by myself, I get on by myself, and I can ride with the best of them. I think it's degrading to allow a man to buy my way into a movie."

After the meeting I sidled up to her.

"You mean what you say?"

"I certainly do."

"Would you like to have a date for the movies Saturday night?"

"Sure, why not?"

"And you want to go Dutch?"

"Absolutely."

Saturday evening I called for her at her dormitory and we walked the half mile to the movie house, discussing equal rights and things like that.

As we neared the box office she opened her purse, took out the price of a ticket, and handed it to me.

"Here, I'm paying my part."

"Oh, no," I said. "You don't give it to me. You pay it at the box office."

"What?"

"Sure. Each pays his own way in. It's the new feminism."

Infuriated and blushing, she paid the cashier, I did the same, and we went in.

I didn't ask her for another date and it was a good thing, too. She reported to others, who reported to me, that I was a real stinker.

63

When I think of college days I think of an awful stunt I pulled on a friend.

I invited him to go home with me for a weekend for some good home cooking and he accepted. As we neared our house I said, "Now, Edward, you know parents these days think college students are a little strange, so we don't want to let them down. At supper tonight there will be an enormous quantity of food on the table and included will be a full pound of homemade butter. Always is. When we're seated, I'm going to pass you the butter and say help yourself. You cut the pound half in two and slide your half onto your plate, then pass the rest to me and I'll slide it onto my plate. Act like it's the normal thing to do."

He grinned. "Good idea. Let's do it."

After grace, I looked over the table loaded with home cooking and picked up the plate of butter.

"Edward, won't you have some butter?" I said.

"Yes, thank you, I believe I will," he said, cutting the pound in two and sliding half onto his plate.

He turned to me. "Won't you have some too?"

"No, thanks," I said. "I don't care for any."

I never could get Edward to visit in my home again.

8

Neighboring Editor

I've been telling you that running a weekly newspaper in a small town is fun—more fun, I believe, than running the *New York Times* or the *Chicago Tribune*, where solemnity is the stern rule and getting fired always a possibility. So to buttress the notion I'd like to report on a friend of mine, now gone, who edited the *Jewett Messenger* for fifty years.

Jack Robinson—that's his name, I didn't make it up—was an expert on human nature and had uproarious fun demonstrating that the human mind has a lot of imagination and all it takes to get it going is somebody to set off the spark.

For example, one week, not having much to write about, Jack printed a paragraph saying huge animal tracks, looking somewhat like those of maybe a gorilla, had been reported seen in the Navasot River bottoms in Leon County. Whatever it was, he said, might account for a few chickens reported stolen.

"Maybe wasn't anything but dog tracks," he wrote. "Did seem a little large for dogs, though, as we know them."

The following week he reported there was a rumor that a gorilla had escaped from a circus train passing through the area, but information on it was hard to get, the matter apparently being hushed up. He said it was just a rumor, probably nothing to it.

After that Editor Robinson didn't have to rely on his imagination any more. His readers were coming to his aid. One man saw gorilla tracks clearly defined in the mud on the Navasota banks. Another came into the *Messenger* office to report fifteen hens missing, the feathers scattered along the river in the woods. Dutifully, Editor Robinson gave light to these reports in print, moving the story up to the top of the front page with a two-column headline: GROWING CONCERN OVER THE GORILLA.

The following week a farmer reported he was missing a calf, the carcass apparently having been dragged out of the barn lot at night. "Took a pretty big critter to do that," he said.

Next week the gorilla itself started showing up. One farmer had seen a dark figure "bigger than a man" moving through the underbrush, his hairy arms swinging.

Another farmer swore he had come face to face with the beast, had seen clearly that it was a gorilla, and had fled when the animal bared its fangs.

Editor Robinson steadfastly set these reports into type.

Dozens of people began getting glimpses of the animal; women and children were staying inside with the doors and windows locked and men were carrying shotguns. Farming was about at a standstill in that area when Editor Robinson decided the thing had gone far enough.

"I was about to believe there was one there myself," he said, his eyes crinkling with pleasure, and he killed the rumors about like he'd started them, saying an overgrown dog had been reported killed in the Navasot bottoms and that must have been what people were mistaking for a gorilla. Said all circuses he'd contacted had denied losing a gorilla. But to this day there are people who will swear they saw a gorilla in the Navasot bottoms.

Political manipulation of the human animal, Editor Robinson demonstrated once with far more finesse than the Watergate gang, is fairly simple.

"There is some talk," he reported in a brief paragraph one week during an election year, "of running Jim Watson for the Legislature."

Now the last thing Jim Watson was considering was running for the Legislature or anything else outside of running his grocery store, and, as far as that's concerned, hadn't anybody else thought of running him.

66

But the day after the paper was out one or two folks dropped by his store and said, "Jim, what's this I hear about you running for the Legislature?" Jim said it was news to him. But you could tell it wasn't an unpleasant thought.

The next week Editor Robinson reported the move for drafting Jim Watson for the Legislature was gaining ground, lots of people saying it was a good idea. (How can you prove whether a lot of people said it or not? the editor said to himself, winking at his dog.) The following week he carried more reports, and the fourth week Jim had thrown his hat in the ring, bought an ad in the *Messenger*, and was running for all he was worth.

There are those who say Jack Robinson stirred up things like this to get some hot campaigns going, thus generating more paid advertising for his paper, but I don't believe it. He wasn't very interested in making money. Although the town had electricity, he ran his press with an ancient gasoline engine and hand-set his type by the light from a window, said if he couldn't earn a living in the daytime he'd try something else. He was haphazard about collecting accounts. One year he went twelve months without presenting the bank a bill for its weekly advertising. When he did get around to it, the banker eyed it closely, harumphed a time or two, and said it seemed a little high.

"If the bank hasn't got the money to pay it, I'll take your note for it," Editor Robinson said.

Only a man who knows human nature could get by with this item buried one week in the "Comings & Goings" column in the *Messenger*: "Sam Plunkett was in town sober Saturday," followed the next week with: "Sam Plunkett is an odd person. He got mad because I said he was sober."

Everybody, including Sam after he'd thought it over, laughed about this, but I'm not good enough to attempt that type of journalism in the *Gazette*.

Jack Robinson knew something about human nature, but that's not to say some people in big cities haven't made a close study of the subject either.

I was opening my mail in the *Gazette* office one morning and ran across a letter from a big magazine saying I may already have won $100,000 if the number on a return card—a number that belongs to me and nobody else—matches a number already selected by a firm of distinguished accountants.

I don't understand. Here's a magazine, a respectable one, with an enormous circulation, offering a million dollars in prizes, including the $100,000 I may already have won, for buying a subscription at about half price. Just return the enclosed numbered order form, the letter says, and if your number is the lucky one, you've won.

"I don't see how they can do it," I said to myself. "Selling subscriptions at nearly half price, then piling a million dollars in prizes on top of that, doesn't make sense."

Moreover, I said, if the winning numbers already are selected, and mine is one of them, and I don't return this order form, what happens?

I decided not to throw their drawings into a tailspin and so returned the numbered form with my subscription check. It's not a bad magazine, and maybe just once I'll be lucky. It's not my worry that the magazine has lost its mind and wants to throw some money around like the federal government.

In a couple of weeks I get this first-class letter from the magazine and out flutters a check for $100,000, made out to me, Harold Smith. Great Scott! You don't mean it! I've actually won! My hands are trembling.

Then I look closer. Well, it's not exactly a check for $100,000. It's made out to me all right and it's for $100,000, but down at the bottom it says this check is not negotiable. The accompanying letter says my name has been selected, that the number on it is my very own and to get in on the final sweepstakes I should return the attached postage-paid card, which also has the same number on it. "You may already have won," it says again.

However, printed on the card there are boxes in which to mark one of two choices. One says "Yes, send me your seventeen-dollar record album of modern song hits," the other, "No, don't send it."

Whether you check "yes" or "no" makes no difference, the letter says; you still have a chance to win up to $100,000.

Here's where a knowledge of human nature comes in.

"Yeah," I say to myself, "you know good and well when all those cards get back to their office, the "yes" cards are going in one pile and the "no" in another, and while a few no cards may win some small prizes, the big money is going to the yes cards." It would be only natural. You'd do it that way too, wouldn't you? I don't know that this is what actually happens, but the notion gnaws at you and, on the eve of winning possibly big money, who wants to take a chance?

Just for once, I said, I believe I'd better gamble $17 for maybe $5 worth of phonograph records against $100,000 in cash.

Then I got to thinking. How many others of the millions who got the same series of letters I got have succumbed to this same line of reasoning? I estimate, knowing how hungry people are for money—especially that big a wad—that at least half will fall for it, if they can scrape up seventeen dollars.

If a million people respond, the magazine will take in seventeen million dollars for some platters that cost possibly five million, with a gross profit of twelve million, less the million in prizes it actually distributes and the cost of promotion.

So that's how a magazine can sell itself at half-price and give away a million dollars to boot.

I declined the offer, but I take my hat off to the genius who thought up the scheme, and so do a lot of respectable magazines who are energetically using the idea.

Makes my turtle look like a cheapskate.

9

The Judiciary in Oat Hill

I've been saying that Oat Hill is a microcosm of the rest of the country, and one more bit of evidence is the court system we've got here.

A trial held in the Altha County Courthouse doesn't attract the attention a sensational big-city trial does, but it's just as slow and drawn-out.

You remember how long it took to try Jack Ruby for shooting Lee Harvey Oswald, despite the fact that he did it in front of television cameras and the deed was seen by practically everybody in the United States? Or to try Sirhan Sirhan?

One Thursday after the *Gazette* was out and I was relaxing and killing some time, I wandered over to the courthouse to listen in on a trial. Beaver Robertson was being tried for setting his car on fire to collect the insurance, and Max Jones, having happened up on Beaver on a country road near Oat Hill just as he threw a match into his gasoline-soaked Chevrolet, had just been called to the stand as a witness.

Now as I understand it, a witness with pertinent information can testify to all he knows, excluding, of course, hearsay, the drawing of conclusions, and such like, but he can't just get up on the stand and tell it; can't volunteer it. It has to be extracted by a lawyer in accordance with some hard and fast rules. The witness can't go from one fact to another; when he finishes one statement, the next one has to be brought out by another question, and it sometimes takes some adroitness to do it under the rules.

For example, here's the scene: Judge Lance is on the bench, the ceiling fan that has needed oiling for several years is laboring overhead, the twelve jurors are settled in the jury box, the prosecution and defense counsel are seated on opposite sides of a long table, and the clerk has just sworn in the witness. Things go about like this:

Prosecution: "Please state your name to the jury."

Witness: "Max Jones."

Prosecution: "Where do you live, Mr. Jones?"

Defense: "Just a minute, I didn't get that name. You say your name is Mack?"

Witness: "No, Max."

Defense: "Macks?"

Witness: "Yes. Ends with an x."

Defense: "Oh, *Max*. Thank you."

Prosecution: "You say your last name is Jones? I want the defense to get this straight."

Witness: "Yes, sir. It's Jones all right."

Prosecution: "It starts with a J?"

Witness: "Yes. J-O-. . ."

Defense: "Just a minute. Your honor, I object. Counsel is leading the witness. The witness is also volunteering information. If he wants to find out how to spell it, let him follow the rules."

Judge: "Objection sustained. Counsel will not lead the witness. The witness will not volunteer any information."

Prosecution: "You say the first letter in your last name is J?"

Witness: "Yes, sir, J."

Prosecution: "All right. Will you now state to the jury the second letter in your last name?"

Witness: "O."

Prosecution: "J-o. All right, will you now tell the jury the next letter in your name?"

Witness: "N."

Prosecution: "Now what is the next letter?"

Witness: "E."

Prosecution: "I believe we now have J-o-n-e, have we not?"

Witness: "Yes, sir."

Prosecution: "Are there any other letters in your name?"

Witness: "Yes, sir."

Prosecution: "Tell the court what it is?"

Witness: "S."

Prosecution: "I see. J-o-n-e-s. Jones?"

Witness: "Yes, sir."

Prosecution: "You're positive there are no other letters in your name?"

Witness: "Yes, sir. That's all. I'm positive."

Prosecution: "I see. So your full last name is Jones? J-o-n-e-s?"

Witness: "Yes, sir. It is."

Prosecution: "Thank you. Your witness, Defense."

Defense: "No questions."

It took a week to try Beaver, and a day and a night for the jury to decide he was guilty. His case is now on appeal.

You think I made this up? You think it didn't take two months to try Sirhan Sirhan when everybody in the whole world knew he shot Bobby Kennedy?

Witnesses usually are at the lawyer's mercy, because the lawyer knows what's going on and the witness doesn't. Now and then, however, a witness will turn the tables.

Ory Keith, a crusty old rancher from the west end of the county, was called to Oat Hill one fall term of district court as a prospective juror in a civil case involving ownership of one-fifth of an acre of land.

A brash young attorney from Houston, representing the defendant, was doing the questioning.

"Do you own your home, Mr. Keith?" he asked.

"Yep, sure do."

"Own anything else?"

"Well, some land around it."

"How much land?"

Ory considered this really none of his business; you don't ask a Texas rancher how much land he has or how many cows, but he mumbled: "Oh, several hundred acres."

"You farm it?"

"Nope. Ranch it."

"You raise cattle?"

"Yep."

"Raise any goats?"

"Goats? Course not." And then as an afterthought: "But I live fairly close to two lawyers."

The court broke up in a roar of laughter.

I ought to point out that I've got several friends in Oat Hill who are lawyers. I was telling one just the other day not to worry about his image, that I'd just read that an opinion poll has found that, in public esteem, lawyers are still three points ahead of chiropractors.

The difference between the high ethical standards of a professional man, like a lawyer or a doctor, and a storekeeper sometimes exists mainly in the professional man's mind.

One day Dr. M. M. Jones, owner of the Jones Hospital and Clinic in Oat Hill, had his nurse call up Joe Hammersmith, who runs a general mercantile store here.

"Joe," the nurse said, "I'm calling for Dr. Jones. He wants to know if you'd like to bid on supplying forty rolls of barbed wire for his ranch. He said to explain that the lowest bidder gets the order."

"Let me figure it up. I'll call you back," Joe said.

He got to thinking about it. "Bid on it? I'm not running a cut-rate store. Why bid on it?" The more he thought about it the less he liked it. He poured himself a stiff drink, propped his feet on his desk and meditated. After a while he called the nurse.

"This is Joe Hammersmith. You tell Dr. Jones I've been sending my family to his hospital for twenty years and never once have I asked him how much he was going to charge me. You tell him if he wants to buy some barbed wire from me I'll sell it to him at my regular price."

Twenty minutes later the nurse called back and said Dr. Jones said go ahead and deliver the forty rolls.

Sometimes professional ethics get stretched a bit on both sides of the fence.

Bill Stockbridge, who runs a prosperous country store five miles out of Oat Hill and advertises once in a while in the *Gazette*, has a sure-fire system for showing a profit.

If an item is selling fast he raises the price on the grounds there's a big demand for it and people will pay more.

If an item is selling slow, he raises the price on the grounds it stays on his shelf longer and therefore requires a bigger markup.

10

Oat Hill Sidelights

If you've read this far—and you must have or you wouldn't be reading this—you may recall that occasionally I've mentioned the courthouse square in Oat Hill and what a preposterous but personally satisfying thing I did to it, which I'll bring out later. But before I get to that I'd like to tell you about some of the Oat Hill citizens.

Literary critics will tell you you're not supposed to interrupt a story, you're supposed to keep the action going, but fifty million television viewers in the United States don't hold with that idea, being able to keep the thread of the story, even if it's interrupted every ten minutes by somebody selling aspirin or shampoo. Shakespeare wasn't above throwing in a few rough-house jokes in the middle of a play as solemn as Hamlet, just to make sure he was bringing something to everybody. He must have known not everyone in the theatre was a Shakespearean scholar. Modern playwrights, on the other hand, are different. They don't think anybody in the audience is a scholar.

(As for jumping around in a book, anybody who has had his credulity wrenched out of socket by modern books like *Catch 22* or *Slaughterhouse Five*, in which characters show up helter-skelter in different disguises in mind-boggling defiance of time, space, and human experience, will certainly allow me a few side excursions.)

Anyway, in the next few episodes, a few sidelights on my favorite town.

75

About the only difference between a sports fan in Oat Hill and one in Dallas or Miami is that we don't boo the quarterback. The referees, that's all right, but not the quarterback. His parents might be in earshot, or his aunts or uncles or cousins. Otherwise, we have the same standards: it's more fun to win and more profitable for the coach and, in the case of the professionals, the owners.

Speaking of professionals, I have long contended that they're making monkeys out of the colleges. A college will take a high school boy, spend real money and time over four years making him into a draft choice, then turn him over scot-free to the professionals.

A hundred thousand people were in the Rose Bowl New Year's Day, 76,000 in the Cotton Bowl, 60,000 in the Sugar Bowl, and about 40 or 50 million others watched the games on television, to climax a season when 21,250,000 people paid about 65 million dollars to see 10 Saturday afternoon games of college football.

And yet, with a box-office smash-hit like this on their hands, what do the colleges do? They close the show and start all over again.

Colleges, in short, are being made monkeys of.

They spend millions of dollars getting teams together that'll attract millions of spectators, then stamp the stars with degrees and turn them over, absolutely free of charge, to a handful of professionals who clean up with them for the next ten years.

It's as though a producer spent millions getting a smash-hit Broadway show together, then, after ten sell-out performances, closed it down and started over on a new one. This is terrible. Why don't the colleges muscle in on the professional football leagues? It would be simple.

Take the colleges in the Southwest Conference, for example. All they'd have to do is add a top layer, called the Southwest Conference College Professional League, and hire a few more coaches, and they'd be in business. They already have the plant—the stadiums, the scoreboards, the dressing rooms, the trainers, the doctors, the training tables, the loyal fans, the bands, the cheer leaders, the mascots, everything.

It's there for the taking. When a high school football star signs a contract for a college athletic scholarship, he signs an added paragraph agreeing to give the college first draft rights to his professional football career.

When his college days are over, he'd automatically graduate to the school's professional team. If he were a quarterback, say, and his school's professional squad already had a quarterback the team's physician estimated was good for five or six more years, give or take a knee operation or two, he could be sold to some other school, to keep the conference in balance.

Freed of the task of attending classes, the graduate football players could practice in the mornings, the regular college players in the afternoons, and the stadium could be used twice a week for games: on Saturdays for the students, so to speak, and on Sundays for the professionals.

For just a small cash outlay, not a third as much as their star players are now receiving as bonuses from the professionals, The University of Texas, Rice, T.C.U., and all the other schools in the Southwest Conference could get into professional football in no time.

If all the other conferences in the country, the Big Ten, the Southeast, the Big Eight, etc., followed the same plan, the new national leagues would be at hand, since professionals, unlike colleges, play each other more than once—it's the only way really to decide who's best and there's a lot more money in it—the winners of each collegiate professional conference, after a full fall of playing every Sunday, could play the semifinals and the finals along in December, with maybe a bowl game or two thrown in around the first of the year. It would be a national sensation; the gate receipts would be astronomical, and the television rights alone would finance many a new campus building, maybe add books to the library, help raise professors' salaries, train more scientists to outwit the Russians, and the like.

Naturally, this would practically pinch off the present professional teams—where would they get any players?—and would put all the profits of football in the hands of the colleges, where it belongs, since they're developing ninety-five percent of the players anyway. It's

77

time to stop letting graduation wreck college football. There's millions in it for higher education.

Also, another notion I haven't gotten anywhere with is a football game in which neither side loses. We swung it with war in Vietnam; leastwise, both sides came out *claiming* they won. But with football, I don't know. I do know it's a shame to realize that half the college students in the nation come away from their stadiums every Saturday afternoon in the fall downcast because their team lost.

I've nearly figured it out, at least to where half the students will be downcast only once a season, which is nine times better than the system we've got.

As you know, touchdowns are the high points of a football game; they're what puts money in the box office and fans on their feet in an uproar.

Therefore, change the rules so the team that scores the most points over the entire season is the winner of a conference. If Texas beats Rice 14 to 12 this Saturday and Rice beats T.C.U. 14 to 12 the next Saturday, Texas and Rice are still tied at 26 all. The race for the championship is still on, and the fans file out of the stadium with hope still aflame and eager for next Saturday's encounter. I can see the headline at the end of the season: TEXAS WINS S.W. CONFERENCE OVER ARKANSAS, 603 TO 596.

But what I started out to tell you about is a football game played in Oat Hill years ago.

The thing, which developed into almost an obsession before it was over, started when Zeke Jones was a senior in high school, captain of the Oat Hill Hornets and a scrappy linebacker and offensive halfback, despite his mere 165 pounds. It was during the annual grudge game between Oat Hill and Castorville, the rivalry between the two comparable to the Thanksgiving Day clash between Texas and Texas A & M.

The game wasn't five minutes old when the referee yelled: "Number 60, you're piling on!" and threw his flag at him.

"Why, I wasn't piling on," Zeke muttered to a teammate. "He wasn't down. Whistle hadn't even blown."

Referee Silas Bickerstaff stepped off fifteen yards for Castorville and the Castorville fans cheered. Cheering when the other side gets a penalty is a sporting oddity prevalent here and, I think, at Harvard too.

Three plays later, on a pass Zeke went back to defend against, Bickerstaff's flag went into the air again as the pass went incomplete.

"Number 60, interference!" he yelled, pointing a finger at Zeke like he had a gun on him, then pulling his arms down in a cradling motion signaling the pass would be considered completed.

"Never touched him," Zeke said to himself.

"What'd you say?" Referee Bickerstaff asked sharply, his hand at the ready to pull his flag again.

"Nothing," Zeke said.

Castorville was now on the Oat Hill five and Zeke, riled and beside himself, charged a split-second before the ball was snapped, caught himself and jumped back without making contact, but up went Bickerstaff's flag. Penalty: half the distance to the goal line. Zeke's insides churned.

On the next play Castorville's fullback plunged over to score and Castorville went ahead six to nothing. The point-after attempt failed.

Late in the fourth quarter, the score was still six to nothing, Oat Hill had the ball and was moving. On a double-reverse that caught Castorville befuddled, Zeke wound up with the ball, circled right end, moved toward the sideline and headed downfield with clear sailing between him and a sure touchdown. As he passed the ten-yard line Referee Bickerstaff's whistle blew, he threw his cap down to mark the spot, waved his arms to stop the clock, and indicated Zeke had stepped out of bounds.

The roar of the crowd drowned out the sound of the whistle and Zeke charged on across the goal line and threw the ball up in the air in the customary jubilant victory sign, circled around in the end zone and waited for his teammate's grateful bear hugs.

They were motioning him to come on back to the ten.

"What's the matter?" he asked between gulps of breath.

"You stepped out of bounds," Bickerstaff said.

"Aw —!" Zeke spit it out, boiling out of control. "By God, I did no such thing. Wasn't two feet from the sideline."

Bickerstaff looked him squarely in the eye. "What'd you say?"

"I said I didn't step out of bounds and, by God, I didn't."

Out came Bickerstaff's flag and down it went at Zeke's feet.

Bickerstaff pocketed his flag, picked up the ball, stepped off a fifteen-yard penalty, faced the stands, and waved his right arm up and down to signal unsportsmanlike conduct.

Time ran out before Oat Hill could get off more than two plays and the game ended, six to nothing, Castorville.

In the dressing room Zeke was inconsolable. "That crooked, blind bastard. Something's got to be done about him. Out of bounds. Off sides. Pass interference. All night long!"

His spirits hung low all weekend; not even his girl could cheer him up.

When the game film was shown Monday morning in slow motion, it could be clearly seen that he had indeed not stepped out of bounds, having been a good two feet inside. Zeke was almost uncontrollable.

"He robbed us of the game," he kept saying. "Bickerstaff robbed us."

When the coach wrote Referee Bickerstaff and reported the film showed Zeke had been in bounds, Bickerstaff replied that you can't always tell by the films and, in his judgment, he was out of bounds. If he was mistaken, he was sorry, but he had to call them like he saw them, and high school boys had to learn this. Furthermore, he would not tolerate profanity in any game he was refereeing.

Everybody else eventually forgot the matter. Injustice to somebody else is easily forgotten. Who remembers what we did to Americans of Japanese descent during World War II? Zeke, however, didn't forget.

The next fall when football again got underway Zeke, now graduated and working in his father's feed store, got into the habit of watching Referee Bickerstaff more than the plays.

"You know what," he decided, "he likes to throw that flag. Must give him a feeling of importance. Look at him. You can tell he's overjoyed when he catches somebody breaking a rule. Watch him sail that flag into the air. Twice as high as necessary. Must give him some sort of pleasure to prance off a penalty. That's when he's in the spotlight, exercising his authority, the damned Nazi.''

All fall Zeke kept his eyes on Bickerstaff, telling himself over and over, there ought to be some way to slow him down.

Friday morning before the final game of the season, once more with arch-foe Castorville, the sky turned dark and rain came down in blinding sheets.

''Gonna be a mud battle tonight,'' somebody said at the Blue Bonnet Cafe while Zeke was drinking coffee.

All morning and into the afternoon the rain continued and along about four o'clock, as Zeke was pulling on his slicker to carry a sack of feed out to a customer's pickup, the idea hit him. It was such a splendid one, he almost threw the sack of feed over the bed of the pickup and into the mud on the other side. ''It just might work,'' he gloated.

Right here you have to understand that in Oat Hill in those days there weren't any seats for football fans. They stood on the sidelines and walked up and down, following the ball, Oat Hill fans on one side, opponents on the other. Just like rugby at Eton.

Zeke arrived at the game that night about five minutes before the kickoff, bundled up in a long, loose-fitting slicker, his hands deep inside the slash pockets, his head covered with a floppy rain hat. A slow misty rain was falling and the field was soft and water-logged. The lights on tall poles only half illuminated the playing field, making it look like a scene from a mystery movie filmed under a dim street light on a foggy London night.

Well, it wasn't much of a game. Three downs slipping and sliding in the mud, then a wobbly kick between fumbles. By the fourth quarter 18 fumbles had occurred, and neither side had got anywhere close to its opponents' goal line. It looked like it would end in a nothing-to-nothing tie. Referee Bickerstaff, mud-soaked and wet, was having a pretty good night though, with 11 penalties for 115 yards already stepped off.

With eight minutes left to play, Castorville had the ball on the Oat

Hill forty and on third down tried an end sweep, coming straight toward the sideline where Zeke was standing. With one hand Zeke unbuttoned his slicker, bent forward slightly, and watched intently.

"Fumble!" the crowd roared, as the wet ball squirted out of the hands of a Castorville back and twenty-two players scrambled for it in the mud.

Zeke made a slight, quick motion with his hands, then faded back into the crowd.

Referee Bickerstaff and the umpire and field judge all dug down into the pile of boys trying to see who had recovered.

Bickerstaff patted a Castorville boy on the back and waved his hand toward the Oat Hill goal line.

"Castorville's ball!" the crowd on the Oat Hill side groaned.

But at exactly the same time, the field judge patted an Oat Hill boy on the back and waved toward the Castorville goal line.

"Oat Hill's ball!" the crowd cried.

Bickerstaff, holding his foot on the ball, looked unbelieving at the field judge, also holding his foot on a ball.

Suddenly it dawned on everybody. There were two balls on the field. *Two balls!* Castorville had recovered one, Oat Hill the other.

Bickerstaff hurried over to the field judge, picked up that ball and looked it over. It was just as muddy and wet as the other one. Regulation size. Same make.

Which was the right one? Was it Castorville's ball and fourth, or Oat Hill's and first?

Bickerstaff was stumped. He was rattled. Give the ball to Castorville and have the Oat Hill fans descend on him, or give it to Oat Hill and get mobbed from the other side? Never in his years of officiating had he run up against anything like this.

He waved his arms to stop the clock, patted himself on the head to indicate it was an official's time-out, and called the other officials over. They talked. They argued. Five minutes passed.

"Hey, Bickerstaff, make up your mind!" Zeke called out. "Thought you knew all the rules."

"Come on, Bickerstaff, it's getting late," another fan yelled.

"Let em play with both balls!" somebody else shouted.

"Who're you gonna penalize this time?" This came from Zeke.

Another five minutes passed. No decision. The crowd was growing restive.

"How about starting over where they were before the fumble?" Bickerstaff suggested to the field judge.

"And give Castorville what'd amount to five downs?" the field judge asked. "You can't do that."

With fifteen minutes gone, the Oat Hill coach got with Castorville's coach and said, "Look, let's call it a tie and go home. Too wet to play football anyway."

"Good idea," he agreed. "Come on boys, we're calling the game off as a tie and going home. Let's get to the showers."

Both teams left for the field house and the fans headed for their cars.

"Wait a minute, you can't do that," Bickerstaff yelled. He blew his whistle to stop the exodus, but nobody paid any attention. He was still standing there when they turned the lights off.

Zeke started his car, first wiping some mud off his hands, and drove home, whistling to himself.

The Shoes on a Lot of Other Feet

Oat Hill, for a long time, was a Prohibition town. About the same percentage of people here like a drink as in Houston or Ithaca, only folks here had to drive forty miles to the nearest wet county.

Editor Clayton Martin of the *Oat Hill News* was an unrelenting dry, in tune with his job as a deacon in the First Baptist Church, and would accept no form of advertising for intoxicants.

Me, I never imposed a moral standard on advertising; if it wasn't illegal and was paid for, I accepted it. Figured if I tried to set up moral standards I'd have to turn down half the political advertising, from candidates for everything from justice of the peace to the presidency, not to mention a considerable amount of merchandise advertising claiming fifty percent off when I knew the price had been marked up fifty percent just ahead of the sale. I've never tried to be the keeper of my brother's morals. Television and I see eye to eye on this.

The beer industry, in a move to soften the opposition in dry areas, worked up an advertising campaign promoting beer as a drink of moderation. "Some people prefer buttermilk, some beer, some tomato juice, but everybody ought to allow the other fellow his choice," the campaign argued.

When the ad campaign was offered to the *Gazette*, I took it. Fifty-two ads, one a week for a year, was not something I turned down. The *New Yorker, Harper's*, and *Playboy* and I see eye to eye on a thing like that.

When the first ad appeared, Editor Martin hit the ceiling and by Sunday was so worked up he had his pastor, the Reverend Horace Lovelace, denounce me from the pulpit.

"Young Editor Smith is a fine young man," the preacher said (a drinking Baptist friend reported his words to me; being a Methodist, I wasn't there), "but he is making a grave error in allowing beer advertising to appear in our midst. For generations Oat Hill and Altha County have been occupied by God-fearing, Christian men and women who know the evils of alcohol, and who know that only misery and degradation come from its use. I call upon the *Gazette* in the name of Christianity to stop this invasion of our area and this violation of our principles. To advertise beer in Oat Hill is to welcome the Devil into our midst. Any man who helps this iniquitous industry, in whatever manner, is committing a sin."

I thought this over for a while, then wrote the following in my personal column:

Since my friend, Rev. Horace Lovelace, has mentioned me in his pulpit and taken the Gazette to task for accepting beer advertising, I'll have to answer him in a similarly public place.

As I understand him, any one in Altha County who helps in the furtherance of beer sales is committing a sin.

You know, just last week I was at Deacon Raymond Woods' service station over on the highway getting a tank of gas when a big trailer truck pulled in. When Raymond finished with me, he walked over and started filling the gas tank of the truck. I looked closely, and you know what? That truck had a sign on its side in letters three feet high: BUDWEISER BEER.

Raymond kept right on filling the tank, even if he is a deacon in the First Baptist Church. Clearly, if Rev. Lovelace is right about this, Raymond should have refused to sell gas to a beer company. Doesn't he know there's no more certain way to further the consumption of beer than by assisting in its transportation? A filling station ought to have as much concern for good people as a newspaper.

Also, I know that the Oat Hill Lumber Company, also run by a Baptist and a deacon to boot, James Partlow, was low bidder on a truck load of lumber week before last to rebuild the Rattlesnake Inn following a fire in that well-known honkytonk over in wet Brazos County. Shouldn't Deacon Partlow have refused to sell lumber for a building to sell beer out of?

And also, there are three or four places in Oat Hill selling radios, when everybody knows the airwaves are filled with beer advertising. Would Rev. Lovelace ask everybody who sells radios to stop and everybody who has one to shut it off because beer advertising is coming into Altha County via the airwaves?

Pick up any daily newspaper or national magazine. You'll find they all contain beer advertising. Would Rev. Lovelace ask everybody to cancel all subscriptions to everything except the Baptist Standard?

Is he going to denounce Deacon Woods and Deacon Partlow and everybody with a radio and a daily newspaper next Sunday?

Saturday morning I got a phone call from Rev. Lovelace.

"Look, Mr. Smith, you understand I'm not backing down on my principles, but I have been talking to some of my members and if you'll agree, I won't say anything more about the *Gazette* if you won't say anything more about my sermon."

I said it's a deal.

Skullduggery is Everywhere

My home wasn't in Oat Hill proper, but about a mile out of town on a small acreage, on the back part of which was an old ramshackle house in which a young man named Dub lived at one time. Dub did odd jobs for me and the rest of the town. He helped some around the *Gazette* plant but his service was limited because he couldn't read or write. You almost have to be able to do one or the other to get very far in the newspaper business.

One year Dub and I went into the chicken business, on a very small scale, on the halves. I guess you could call it on the halves. I furnished the chickens and the feed, Dub looked after them, and the deal was that when they became frying size we'd split fifty-fifty.

About the time I figured the chickens ought to be ready to put in my

85

freezer I walked back to Dub's house and asked how they were coming along.

"Say, I been meaning to tell you," Dub said, "You had hard luck with your chickens."

"That so? What happened?"

"The hawks got in and killed most of them."

"Didn't they get any of your half?"

"Oh, naw sir, I'd already sold my half some time back."

I've often thought, if Dub had learned to read and write, no telling how far he could have gotten in life. Might even have become a White House aide.

Nudity in Oat Hill

I'll have to admit the movies, the stage, and now even grand opera have Oat Hill beat all hollow when it comes to showing up in the raw. Even so, this town is not without something to offer in that line, however unplanned.

People still laugh when they recall what happened to Barney Searcy, though it was years ago and was never printed in the *Gazette*. Some city dailies are now rejecting advertising for x-rated movies, but the *Gazette* long ago took the lead in this by rejecting even x-rated news stories.

Barney Searcey was a gnarled-knuckled plumber and a good one, with a strong feeling for what he considered decency. Couldn't even bring himself to change the rubber gasket under a commode if the woman of the house was near at hand; it'd be as unthinkable as a loyal British subject's imagining the Queen's ever having to go to the bathroom herself.

One day he got a call from Mrs. Hortense Bowers saying the lavatory in her bathroom was stopped up.

"I may be gone when you get here but come on in and fix it," she told him. "When do you think you can get here?"

"Oh, in about an hour, Mrs. Bowers," Barney said.

Thinking she had plenty of time, Mrs. Bowers decided to take a bath before leaving for the Wednesday afternoon meeting of the Methodist Woman's Missionary Society.

86

Barney, getting through with a job in his shop quicker than he'd figured and not paying any attention to the time, drove up to Mrs. Bower's house, got out his tools and went in. When he pushed open the bathroom door and saw Mrs. Bowers stark naked in the tub he almost fainted. She screamed and he hit his head on the door facing backing out, dropping two wrenches as he fled through the front door. He jumped in his truck, gunned the motor, and spun his tires as he sped away.

Aghast, he didn't know what to do but keep driving fast. He drove all the way over to Castorville, pulled out onto a country road, and sat there the rest of the afternoon, seeing his whole life unreeling before him as though he were drowning. He thought of driving to Oklahoma and asking somebody in Oat Hill to ship his tools to him.

Well, after dark he decided it was too late in life to start up a new business in Oklahoma, he might as well go back to Oat Hill and face whatever awaited him. He eased into his garage, slipped into his house, crawled into bed and stayed there all night and the rest of the next day. Nobody knows how long he would have stayed there if Mrs. Bowers hadn't called to say, "Forget it, I still want that lavatory unstopped," or if she hadn't thoughtfully assured him that she was going shopping and would not be around when he got there, *for sure*.

Modesty is one thing, but a good plumber is hard to find.

By the way, x-rated movies are now being shown occasionally in Oat Hill with uneven success, the same as in the cities. Attendance spurted at first but is falling off now. Most people here aren't shocked by them, just bored.

This Side of Heaven

This morning my pastor came into the *Gazette* office, shook hands, and announced that he was puzzled.

"What about?" I asked.

"People," he said. "It's a funny thing, here we're having all sorts of trouble raising this year's church budget, and yet the people of this town have just contributed $300,000 to build a new hospital. I don't understand it."

"Well, preacher, it looks to me like people will pay more readily to stay out of heaven than to get there."

He shook his head. I nodded mine.

Off-Color

Speaking of shaking hands, while this is not an off-color book, earthy humor surfaces in Oat Hill the same as it does on Broadway or in the movies, although I think ours is less commercial.

Our undertaker, Ray Connell, is the handshakingest man in four counties, the same as undertakers in Houston or New Orleans or San Francisco. Meet him on the street and his right hand shoots out as automatically as an electric-beam-controlled door opens when you step in front of it.

One morning Lee Lewis parked his pickup and horse trailer in front of the Blue Bonnet Cafe, looked up the street and saw Ray handshaking his way down the block. He stepped out of his truck, went back to the horse trailer and got a right handful of something very fresh, stepped back onto the sidewalk with his hand behind his back, and waited.

"Why, hello, Lee, mighty glad to see you," Ray said, extending his hand.

"Sure glad to see you, Ray," Lee said, accepting the handshake with an extra warm squeeze.

Ray looked down at his hand, tried to smile, and hurried off to the lavatory in his undertaking parlor.

It didn't stop him from shaking hands but it sure crimped his style for a while.

Those sidelights took up more room that I'd figured but a book, like a loaf of bread, has to have a middle because who wants nothing but end slices? Or like a freight train. There's no money in an engine pulling a caboose.

I will now tell you what a shameful thing I did to the courthouse square in Oat Hill.

I I

The Old Codgers on the
Courthouse Square

The *Gazette* occupied a thirty-foot-wide brick building on the southeast corner of the courthouse square in Oat Hill. It was one of those split-front buildings. A partititon divided it exactly in half for about twenty-five feet back, making room for two offices in the front.

The *Gazette* had the office on the east side of the partition, plus the rest of the area to the back of the building. Cornelius Wolfe, who believed in fatalism, had a barber shop in the other office. "You won't die till your time comes," he believed. "What if I jump off this building and kill myself, when I'm not supposed to die for years yet?" you could ask him, but he had the answer ready! "That's where you'd make a mistake. Your time was then, not later." I never could follow this very clearly but it seemed to make sense to Cornelius. I guess if philosophy was easy to understand most philosophers would have a hard time making a living.

The building was owned by Jim Bowers, a crusty old skinflint and a tough customer to deal with except when you were handing him the rent money. I found out long ago it was easier, and I guess cheaper in time and nervous tension, to go ahead and fix anything that needed fixing on the building from time to time rather than confronting Mr. Bowers with the problem and having him argue against it, put it off, and tell you how hard times are and how little you can make out of rent property.

One spring day the awning in front of the building broke loose from

89

the iron chain that held it up and one corner sagged. Here was a problem I figured I didn't have to attend to; it was an unsightly thing, hanging there like a rock ledge fixing to fall, and moreover, it was dangerous. Mr. Bowers waited around a whole day, hoping I'd give in; but I didn't, and the next morning he had Rastus Cox, the poorest excuse for a carpenter in Altha County—and the lowest paid—jacking up the awning and pulling it back into place.

"Mr. Bowers," I said. He was leaning against the plate glass window in front of the *Gazette* office supervising the work. "How old is this building?"

"Oh, don't know, pretty old. Still a mighty good building, though. Why?"

"Aw, just wondering. Just wondering how much it cost to build."

"Cost plenty, I imagine. Course in those days things weren't so high. Labor a lot cheaper. Rastus there right now is costing me sixty-five cents an hour. Ain't worth it, but what's a man gonna do? Unions and all, everybody organized."

If there was a union in Altha County, outside of the Baptist Training Union, I never heard of it.

"Mr. Bowers, how long have you owned this building?"

"Oh, let's see, I bought this building about forty-five years ago. Why?"

"Oh, nothing, I was just wondering how much you've made off it. I've been in it twelve years myself. Used to pay fifteen dollars a month, then you went up to twenty-five, then to thirty, and now you're sticking me for forty dollars."

"Sticking, nothing. It ought to be higher. Ain't no money in rent property. Time you pay these high taxes, high insurance, keep up the repairs constantly, ain't nothing left. One of the poorest investments there is, rent property."

"Mr. Bowers, would you sell me this building?"

"Nope."

"I believe I could pay cash for it, if it wasn't too high." I had about $3,500 in the bank and knew I could borrow the rest. I've forgotten to mention it but the *Gazette* by now was a pretty successful paper, had around $20,000 worth of new equipment, and a good stock of newsprint, and my income was about three or four times what a reporter was making on a daily paper in Houston or Dallas. I owned my home, which I had built on the edge of Oat Hill, had a wife and two children, and drove a good car, which I always paid cash for. I guess you might say that for a financial structure built originally on the back of a turtle I was, in my small way, as substantial as the Astors, who built theirs on the backs of Indians and fur trappers. Other people in this world had a lot more money than I, but my Chevrolet was just as paid for as their Cadillacs and the steaks I ate were just as thick. The democratic thing about a steer is it produces no better steak for a rich man's money than it does a small man's. It's true I can't afford a yacht but I don't know a single millionaire who can afford a battleship. We all have our limitations. You can get from Oat Hill to Houston in the same time in either a Chevrolet or a Cadillac; so I can't see how it makes much difference which you're in and, blindfolded, I doubt if you could tell. The airconditioning in mine is just as cool.

"No, wouldn't be interested in selling at all," Mr. Bowers said.

I left him standing there and went back inside my office. Housing the *Gazette* in my own building had become a minor obsession with me. Publishing your own newspaper is one of the most soul-satisfying things on earth, but operating in a rented building takes away some of your independence. There was always the feeling that I wasn't quite free, that there was still one man who, out of a clear sky, without considering my wishes, could tell me to move. Back in the Depression, when I had started the paper, God bless Methuselah, you could lease a building in Oat Hill for about as long as you wanted, but now every building around the square was filled. So were most of those on the streets running off from the square, and about a two-year lease was all you could get. I didn't even have a lease from Mr. Bowers; rental was on a month-to-month basis. Any morning he could give me thirty days to move out and I'd have to. Even the county clerk had more tenure than that, so long as he wasn't caught stealing.

When Mr. Bowers let me know he was going to continue sacrificing and hold on to his rent property I decided to try elsewhere and walked around the square to Tom Webb's office, upstairs over the First National Bank. Tom is a real estate man.

"Come in, Harold, sit down and rest yourself." Tom was sitting at his desk looking out the window watching the traffic around the square. "What you got on your mind?"

"Nothing much, just wandering around."

"Whatcha cooking up now? Working on a special edition to trap the President of the United States?"

"Naw, just an idea I have to abolish real estate agents."

"I'm for it. Business dull anyway."

"Say, Tom, you know property in Oat Hill pretty well, is there anybody on the square who'd sell me his building?"

"Sure. Al Stockard will."

"He will?" I brightened.

"Sure. For twenty thousand dollars."

"Twenty thousand! Oh, I guess he would. But seriously, I sort of want to own my own building. Isn't there anybody around here who'll sell?"

Now you've got to understand there's a little difference between the growth problems of a county-seat town like Oat Hill and a city like Houston. Down there the courthouse doesn't mean much; it can be stuck off anywhere. But in Oat Hill the courthouse square is square, one block in each direction, hence the possibilities for expansion are limited to the four sides. Sure, some businesses go up or down on one of the four streets running onto the square, but to be in the main stream of things you've got to be on the square. In Oat Hill the side streets were good enough for lumber yards or feed stores or shoe repair shops. But the square is the only place for the Fifth Avenue section. The ladies' shops, the hardware stores, the two banks, the drug stores, the cafes, the dry goods stores, and the newspapers.

I could buy a lot off the square and put up a building, but in Oat Hill that's openly conceding you've been elbowed out. Besides, a newspaper in a small town needs to be near the center of things. An editor needs to make the transition from his typewriter to the business community without having to hike. You see a man on the street you want to talk business to, you want to be able to say, let's step into my office a minute; you don't want to have to say, let's get in the car and ride to my office. There's a delicacy about editing a paper, particularly if you've got competition. You're sensitive about making a display of some people you're talking to, or what you're lining up, and a lot of people are sensitive about talking to one editor more than the other. Most people in business in a small town are on such delicately balanced footing they have to watch themselves constantly. They've got to deal with the same customers over and over. Somebody goes up to Charles Parker, who's trying to carry on his father's dry goods business without enough capital, and says, "Say, Charles, I saw you driving down to the *Gazette* office this morning. What you got brewing? Got a sale coming up? You taking sides in the school trustee election?" And Charles doesn't like it. But when your newspaper office is right on the square a man can walk in casually, like he was just going in to chat, and nobody pays any attention.

Tom Webb shook his head. "If you can buy a building on this square you can beat me."

"Well, keep your ears open, Tom. If you ever do hear of anything, let me know about it first, will you?"

"Sure will, Harold, but don't count on it."

Once I get interested in a problem it stays with me. I catch myself thinking about it at odd moments, like while I'm listening to a sermon or while my wife is talking at the supper table or while I'm reading the paper at night.

One morning at the office I drew up a rough ownership map of the square, listed everybody around it, his business, my estimate of his financial condition. In the same building with me was Cornelius Wolfe's barber shop. Next to him was the Denson Grocery Store, then the Knight Furniture and Mortician—that's the way the sign read then— the Brown Dry Goods Store, etc. There were four grocery stores around the square, two cafes, eight dry goods stores, two hardware stores, and the two picture shows—the Palace for first run shows and the Rix for westerns and second runs. The First National Bank was on the northwest corner of the square, the Farmers State about the middle of the block on the north side. There were also two auto supply stores, three drug stores, another furniture store, a couple of variety stores, two novelty shops, and four barber shops. No use naming them all, but around the square there were about 55 businesses on the ground floor, plus law offices, beauty shops, a photographic studio, real estate offices, and insurance offices, upstairs in the two-story buildings. We had no building taller than two stories. In Dallas, builders have to go up twenty-five or thirty stories before they catch on there's no point in going any higher. In Oat Hill we caught on at the second story. When you think about it, the Empire State Building in New York, with its 120 stories, is just a monotonous repetition of a two-story building we've had in Oat Hill since before the Civil War.

Owning a building on the square wasn't so much evidence of shrewdness as good fortune, a point I'm sure Henry Ford III will appreciate. Some people owned a place on the square now because luck had taken care of them, half of them had tried to sell at one time or another in long years past, before the town had built up and when the square was still gap-toothed with vacant lots. As the town grew, the highway came through, and more buildings were put up, even a moron could then see owning a piece of property there was a pretty good thing and everybody hung on. Half the businesses around the square were operated by sons or sons-in-law of men who had got there first and got title to the frontage.

I don't mean to say none of the buildings could be bought if you wanted to pay three or four times what they were worth. Two days after I'd talked to Tom Webb, Al Stockard came to me and said, "Say, Harold, I understand you're in the market for a building. I'll sell you mine, let you pay for it anyway you want to, terms as long as you want."

"How much you want for it, Al?"

"I'll take two thousand dollars down and the balance in fifteen years."

"The balance? How much is the balance?"

"Eighteen thousand, and it's worth it."

"Who you kidding, Al? You'll have to move that building to Houston before you can get that kind of money."

Another time old man Jake Bowman, who'd been a lawyer in Oat

Hill for 50 years, waddled down from his upstairs office in the building he owned and came over to the *Gazette* office with an air of importance like he was bringing me an appointment as ambassador to the Court of St. James. Clearing his throat, he announced he'd heard I was interested in buying a lot in Oat Hill and he had just the thing. Turned out it was a lot two blocks from the square, all he wanted for it was $3,000, and all it had cost 25 years ago when he bought it at a tax foreclosure sale was $140.

"That's too far off the square, Judge," I told him.

"Oh, I don't know. About as close as you can get. Not many newcomers can get even that close." I was still a newcomer to the judge, although I'd been there twenty years. Everybody was a newcomer to the judge unless he had been born there, with the exception of his father, a pioneer, who had arrived at the site when it was covered with prairie grass. The reason he'd stopped there was that a wheel on his wagon had collapsed and he didn't have money enough to buy another one and the blacksmith wouldn't sell him one on credit.

Still, I wanted a building of my own on the square. Editor Martin of the *News* seemed satisfied to rent; been in the same building 40 years and, as far as I know, he liked the arrangement. Renting irked me. Capitalism runs deeper in me than it does in some people, I guess.

12

A Million Dollars

What I'm going to tell you from here on out won't be hard to believe if you believe an Associated Press news story I clipped out of the paper the other day:

> FRESNO, Calif. (AP)—Mrs. Cora Nidever, 85, who made an oil fortune on 80 acres of barren land she inherited, left an estate in excess of two million dollars, including $1,872,350 in cash. She died a week ago after a long illness.
>
> Mrs. Nidever inherited the property near Coalinga, Calif., from her mother, Mrs. Hester Binkley, who had homesteaded it at the turn of the century. Oil was discovered on it in 1939.

I'm not making this up; I really clipped the above out of the *Houston Post*. Such stories crop up in the news every once in a while.

Sometimes fortune reaches out blindly and picks up somebody by the scruff of the neck and sets him up in almost limitless wealth with the impartiality of lightning. Stop and think; you probably can name a millionaire who got rich without much effort on his part. Sheer luck. This isn't to say a lot of millionaires didn't work hard; some probably worked four times as hard as most people before they became millionaires and by that time most of them don't know anything else to do except to keep on working. It's all right with me.

One of the entrancing things about capitalism is that occasionally it does lift a man up out of the humdrum of earning a living and barely getting by and place him on an economic throne. After living constantly with the fear of slipping or making too many mistakes, or slowing down, or having to go to the hospital, and having the hounds catch up with him and pull him down into economic ruin, a man suddenly is handed so much money that the last trace of economic fear is removed. For the first time in his life he can buy without considering cost and spend without fear of overdrawing.

I know some people consider this aspect of capitalism wholly unfair, holding that a man isn't entitled to something he didn't earn, but that's an extremely unpoetic view of life, rejected even by a Russian premier as he leaves his luxurious town house for a vacation at his summer place in the country. Who's to say Byron, who could bake his brain while lying in front of the fireplace, then jump up and pour himself out spontaneously in deathless poetry, earned his talent? Do you think Mozart, composing complicated music at the age of five, acquired the knack by hard work? You think Communism will ever manage to give every brain the same IQ? Or everybody a villa as luxurious as the premier's?

Capitalism not only gives a man the best chance of any system to get and enjoy what he earns; it goes that one better and holds out the wonderful opportunity to get far more than he earns. As far as I'm concerned, that enhances capitalism and takes some of the boredom out of life.

Of course I'll admit that when some people acquire this disproportionate share of wealth they don't know what to do with it, spending it in riotous living, as they say, like Onassis putting gold handles on the bathroom fixtures on his yacht and covering his bar stools with leather made from whales' testicles. Others, given a million dollars, can think of nothing that's any more fun than using it to make another million. They then proceed to get on so many boards of directors that their time is no longer their own and they have less fun than before they struck wealth. Others contribute to politicians and get appointed to some office where the exercise of power, however limited and unimportant, feeds their ego.

Actually, few people who get smiled on by fortune in a big way seem to know what to do with it, and you may say that I was one. I wouldn't. I think I had more fun with mine than anybody I ever heard

97

of, and it only bore out my theory that a man can have as much fun in a small town as he can in a city or any place else.

Here's how it happened.

My father was a small town banker. Not a millionaire by a long shot. I don't think he wanted to be, but he was financially successful. When he made some money over and above what it took to educate his family, he invested it in land.

When he died he left me 500 acres of ranch land in West Texas. Five hundred acres in some places is a lot of land; in West Texas it's just a smidgin. Those 500 acres were rocky, brush-covered land that cost $5 an acre and would support about 10 cows, which isn't enough to fool with from a distance. The only revenue I'd been getting from it came from a grazing lease that paid me $125 a year. A neighboring rancher who had 30,000 acres was kind enough to keep the fences up on my 500 acres and pay me two bits an acre per year for grazing privileges. After I paid the taxes I had around $100 a year income from the thing, but there was considerable satisfaction in referring occasionally to my West Texas holdings, and I never tried to sell it.

One day, I remember it was in the spring, I had just returned from the post office with an armful of mail, mostly newspapers from fellow weekly publishers, and was sorting out the first-class letters. I always opened the envelopes that looked like they might have checks from advertisers first, then those that looked like ad orders from the agencies, saving the duller looking ones till last. The last letter I opened that morning was from the O'Toole Oil Company, asking if I would be interested in leasing my 500 acres in West Texas for a wildcat oil exploration? The company offered 50 cents an acre for this privilege—a total of $250. It made me feel pretty good, like winning a poker pot with a pair of deuces.

Being a man who answers his mail promptly, I wrote "O.K." on the bottom of the letter, signed my name, addressed an envelope and was reaching for a stamp when Harry Gilcut came in. Harry knows more jokes than anybody in Oat Hill and those word-of-mouth stories that sweep the country—by African drum signal, I guess—without ever getting into print never failed to reach him first.

"Come in, Harry," I said.

98

"Say, have you heard about how dry it is out in West Texas?" He spoke as he entered the door and I knew this one was fairly clean because Carolyn, my reporter, was at work in earshot and Harry is on the Board of Stewards of the Methodist Church.

As Harry reached for a chair I put a stamp on the letter and, instead of dropping it in the cigar box on the side of my desk I use for outgoing mail, I laid it on the desk. My desk, like many country editors' desks, stays littered, and that's the reason I got rich.

"Nope, haven't heard it. How dry is it out there?"

"Why, it's so dry out there it's easier to make a horse drink than it is to lead him to water."

Harry always busts out laughing, too, when he tells a joke, makes no difference how many other times he's told it the same day. It improves the humor, which is the reason radio and television comedians perform before a studio audience, or have the sound of laughter dubbed in. The laughter is the key—frequently the only one—to the millions of listeners that something funny has been said.

Harry lowered his voice and told me a couple more. They were fair, although I never cared much for that kind, and I said, "Come on, I'll buy you a drink," and we went out to the Blue Bonnet and had coffee. By the time I got back to the office, Clyde had left a stack of proofs on my desk and I fell to reading. I had to check one of the proofs against the copy and in rummaging through the typed sheets I ruffled up my desk a little. Through a strange and inscrutable working of fortune, I accidentally shoved the letter to the O'Toole Oil Company under the litter of paper on my desk, and there it stayed.

Two hundred fifty dollars, out of a clear sky, is a nice thing to have happen to you. Starting a week after I thought I'd mailed that letter, I never went to the post office but what I looked for it. A letter with the return address of the O'Toole Oil Company had taken on even more appeal than an ad order, but I looked in vain. After a few weeks I supposed O'Toole had come to its senses and had no intention of giving me $250.

Three and a half months later, along in late summer, I opened the *Dallas News* one morning and sat up erect when a headline caught my eye: WEST TEXAS OIL STRIKE REPORTED.

An oil well, it said, had suddenly blown in at 2,800 feet on a wild-cat test the O'Toole Oil Company was drilling. The oil was going over the top of the derrick and running wild, catching everybody off guard as geologists had calculated oil wouldn't be hit above the 4,000 foot depth, and O'Toole must have believed them. Oil geologists are like doctors; they frequently don't know any more about what's inside than you do, till they open up and see.

In the oil business in Texas everything generally is played close to the chest. They've got lots of turtle handlers in the business. A company will put down a test well in a new area, drill for a month, pull down the rig, and move away. Another dry hole, is the report, and landowners in the area who'd been holding out for higher lease money kick themselves and mope around. Then maybe in a year some stranger with threadbare pants shows up, offers to pay 50 cents an acre for leases, and leases up the entire area. Those landowners aren't going to make the same mistake twice. Whereupon the original company takes over the leases and drills another well and finds oil. This saves a lot of money on leases and the oil they discovered a year before and kept quiet about was perfectly safe, stored underground where it had been for millions of years.

But where O'Toole made its mistake was in hitting a gusher. There's no hiding that. When the drill bit hits the pressurized pool, oil just busts loose and shoots over the derrick and the fat's in the fire. O'Toole hadn't been too bent on getting my 500 acres under lease; it had the 30,000 acres of the rancher nearby and a lot more. If no oil was discovered, it wasn't interested in mine anyway; if a good showing was found, it could be kept underground until the lease block was completed.

But a gusher, that's like getting caught with the bank loot in the back of your car five minutes after the hold-up, and me with 500 acres of unleased land in the center of a real oil field was an entirely different story. The gusher wasn't over 500 yards from my land.

Before noon that day I'd had two long distance telephone calls. The first caller offered me $10 an acre. He was taking one of those long shots with somebody unfamiliar with the facts, a practice that sometimes pays off, but I wasn't that unfamiliar. I may kid the *Dallas*

News some, but you can get more hard news out of it than most papers, and it was on the job with that oil news. The second one offered me $50. I could already figure that was $25,000 and I was tempted, but things were moving too fast and I said I'd have to think it over.

"Better take me up. That field may not go in your direction," the voice on the phone said. But I said he could contact me later.

By next morning I was being called on in person. When an oil strike is made, lease hounds, little ones and big ones, converge on the area and comb the courthouse records for unleased land, land with cloudy titles, and other windfalls. The West Texas records had been combed.

At ten o'clock that morning two Cadillacs, three Buicks, and four Chevrolets were parked in front of the *Gazette* office, and I was being seen by appointment only.

The bidding for my five-hundred-acre lease got so fast and competitive that I was beginning to wish the thing hadn't happened, but I managed to push the feeling aside. I had so many offers for lunch I turned them all down and went home at noon to get some thinking done, but there was one man from a major oil company who was smart enough to find out where I lived. He gave me thirty minutes to get home and eat before his Cadillac pulled up in the driveway and he knocked on my door.

"Mr. Smith," he said after we were seated in the living room, "my company wants a lease on your land. We got slipped up on; we don't have an acre of land under lease in that area and we want in on that pool of oil."

I was listening pretty hard and I had a feeling he was on the level. He continued.

"I know you're smart enough to know you've got a mighty valuable piece of property. We know it too, and we're not trying to see how little we can get it for. We're going to see how much we can pay for it. Your land is only five hundred yards from the discovery well and it's got lots of oil under it, at a depth we can drill to and make money."

Here he cleared his throat and looked me straight in the face.

"Mr. Smith, will you take two thousand dollars an acre for a lease on your land?"

"Yes sir," I said, "I will." It was sort of like answering the preacher at your wedding; you don't take time to mull over the answer, you come out with "I do" automatically, to get the thing over with in a hurry, since you'd already figured you were getting a good deal. In consideration for my intelligence, however, I ought to say that just before I said yes, or maybe simultaneously, my brain clicked fast enough to register with me that 2,000 times 500 is one million.

"All right," he said, "the next question is, will you get in the car with me and go to Houston right now and sign the lease?"

"Why not?" I said.

We were in Houston in two hours and up on the fourteenth floor of the company's building ten minutes later. My lease was signed and put in escrow in a Houston bank with a check for one million dollars, the check to be delivered to me and the lease to them after their attorneys had checked the title to the land, which I already knew was good because Papa had bought enough land in his lifetime to take care of such details.

I guess the most delightful ride I've ever had was the one back to Oat Hill. The oil company executive offered to send me back in his car, but I rode the bus. I wanted to be alone with my thoughts. I had plans to make and the material to make them with. I was the richest man in Oat Hill. Next man to me probably was Jim Bowers, who was reputed to be worth around $200,000, depending on how you figured his buildings and farm land. But mine was in cash, minus what the income tax took, and there was the comforting thought that I hadn't sold the 500 acres, only leased them, and one-eighth of all the oil produced on the tract would be mine for as long as the oil was brought up. The income was additionally shielded by that 27½ percent depletion allowance, which up to that time I had been editorializing against. I've heard that the way to make an economics professor more conservative is to double his salary.

Would I show a few people! Wait till the news got out. Some people are lifted up, transported, by various things in their lifetime. Some by winning the girl they seek, others by finally paying for their home, a few by hearing from a publisher that their book has been accepted, some by having a son born; but I doubt if there's anything in the world so calculated to lift a man's spirits sky high as the sudden realization that he has a million dollars in cash. Down drop all the old worries, up surge all the unrealized desires. The thought of uncontested, unassailable economic independence, the absolute freedom from pressure of survival, to one who has been under such pressure all his working life, is about the most exhilarating feeling the human breast can have. You can call this crass if you want to, and maybe it is, but it's mighty close to the truth.

The first few miles out of Houston I leaned back in my seat and gloated. All the daydreams I'd ever had fell away as foolishness in the face of the greater reality of that check lying in the bank in Houston and a copy of the escrow agreement in my pocket.

What would you do if you had a million dollars? It was a question I hadn't given much thought to, no more than I had to wondering how far out space extends. The question now was the most intriguing I'd ever encountered. Never was the scenery more beautiful than the pine trees speeding past me as the bus raced toward Oat Hill.

By the time the bus stopped in front of the Blue Bonnet, I had arrived at a plan.

It would be known that I had leased some land to an oil company; you can't have that many oil company people parked in front of your office in Oat Hill without the story spreading. But it wouldn't be known, I decided, how much I'd gotten. Other people in Oat Hill have received oil lease money; old Jake Bowman, the lawyer, got a royalty check every month, for fifteen dollars, but it would never occur to anybody to think in terms of thousands of dollars, not to mention a million.

The knowledge that other people know you have a million dollars may be pleasurable to some millionaires, particularly if they're short on inner resources, but to me the knowledge that I had it and that nobody else knew it opened up far more possibilities.

First, I said, I'm going to buy a building on the square. I don't care what it costs, I'll buy it. There were other things crowding into my mind I wanted to do, but owning a building for my newspaper had obsessed me for so long it was my first objective, now that overwhelming somebody with enough money was all it took.

People would see some unmistakable signs of affluence as I relaxed and did the extra things for my family I hadn't done before, but affluence in a small town is anything from five thousand dollars in cash on up to say twenty-five or thirty thousand; nobody assumes anybody in a small town has any more cash on hand than that, unencumbered and available for spending, and nobody has, except on a one-in-a-million chance like mine.

I thought I would buy Harry Gilcut a hat, in appreciation for making me forget to mail the letter to O'Toole, and would let him know why, up to a certain point.

Cautiously but not without confidence, I waited for the title to be examined. It was about ten days later, with assurance mixed with unsteadiness, that I guardedly opened in the post office an envelope from Houston—not being able to wait till I got back to the office—and saw a green check fastened with a paper clip to the letter of transmittal. It was, indeed, for one million dollars.

I pushed it back in the envelope, shoved it in my pocket, bundled up the rest of the mail, and practically floated back to my office.

For a few minutes I sat at my desk and—I admit it—fondled that check and glowed. I had a pleasurable desire to stretch this moment out as long as I could. But after a while I picked up an envelope, addressed it to the same bank in Houston, endorsed the check "For deposit only," and took it around to the post office and mailed it. The last place I wanted that money was in an Oat Hill bank. I wouldn't get out the bank's front door before the news would be all over town.

Back in my office, I looked at my check stub and noticed I had $3,221.53 in the First National Bank in Oat Hill, $738 in the Farmers State. While a month previously these accounts had seemed substantial, now the total was a mere pittance. But I was the only one who could appreciate the humor, and I intended to keep the joke to myself.

I rubbed my hands in anticipation. "Now I'm going to buy a building on the square."

I guess I'm odd, but I'm not like a lot of other people. You take some people and capitalize them so substantially they're no longer obliged to do whatever they've been doing to earn a living, and they'll pull up short. Most of them will quit and try something else.

Most people aren't unhappy with what they're doing but on the other hand they aren't fascinated either. Put in a position where they're no longer required to earn a living, most of them would put on their hat and walk off the job. Why, I suppose there are even lots of preachers who, if suddenly handed wealth, would reinterpret the original call they'd had from on High and tell a lot of parsimonious deacons and hypocritical stewards where they could go. I don't know what percentage would do this, but I have a notion.

But running the *Gazette* wasn't something I was doing because I couldn't do something else; don't classify me with preachers, grammar school principals, and army officers. It's a fascinating way to earn a living, to express yourself, if you want to put it that way, to establish your own independence; it's a game you can play endlessly. It's pleasant to publish what you write without having to ask somebody else if it's good enough, particularly an editor for some big outfit who's not much of a writer himself. I made good money at it but I suppose I could have made more in some other line of work, something devoted more nearly exclusively to making money and less to expressing and indulging your mental self, say insurance or medicine.

Therefore, with a million dollars, less taxes, in the bank, my first thoughts were unashamedly of the *Gazette*. Admittedly, I was going to slack up a little on some of the details, like reading proof. I was going to hire another reporter and get out from under the compulsion of meeting all the deadlines myself, but I was going to continue to edit the paper and be a part of Oat Hill and Altha County.

With my old chart of the square before me, I sat down in my office and began figuring where I'd buy a building. Once more I made the rounds, taking my time and asking every owner if he'd sell. If a man needed the building he was in, I didn't press him; just asked if he'd sell, thanked him when he said no, and moseyed on. But with one of these fellows who didn't need a building, like Jim Bowers, who had five, or Tom Carrington or Jake Bowman, who had two a piece, I went into my case more thoroughly.

"How can a man ever get to own his own building in this town if some of you fellows with more than you need won't sell?" I asked Jim Bowers.

"That's not my problem," he said with a cold grin.

"But I'm willing to pay all it's worth, maybe a little more, and cash too."

Mr. Bowers just shook his head.

Next I tried Jake Bowman. He wasn't interested, until I said I might be willing to pay a pretty steep price.

"How much would you give me for my building on the east side of the square?" he asked.

"Oh, I don't know, it probably cost two thousand dollars when it was built, but the town has grown and property's worth more now; it's probably worth six or seven thousand, but I'll give you ten thousand in cash for it right now."

"Ten thousand! Why what are you talking about?" He was sputtering in his outraged courtroom manner. "Why that building's in the best location in town. I'll sell it to you for twenty thousand but not a penny less."

For a moment I was tempted. I came within an inch of saying "All right, Judge, I'll take it. Draw up a deed and I'll have the money ready." But something stopped me. I think maybe my mind was already working on a plan it hadn't informed me of yet, and I found myself saying, "Well, Judge, that's more than twice what that building's worth or ever will be worth." I thanked him and left, fighting off the temptation to ask him for how much he had rendered that twenty-thousand-dollar building for taxes. It wasn't over $1,500, but I didn't see any point in riling him up when there was nothing to be gained by it.

It was the same with Tom Carrington, only he was even colder and more contemptuous.

"Why I wouldn't sell you one of my buildings under any circumstances. Newspapers are here today and gone tomorrow. It'd take you the rest of your life to pay that building out."

When I tried to tell him I wanted to pay cash, he wouldn't even listen. "Aw, where would you get that much cash?" He was a director in the Farmers State Bank and knew the bank balance of everybody in town.

All around the square it was about the same story. Al Stockard, having just happened to bump into me got wind of my offers to pay cash, and again offered me his run-down building for twenty thousand dollars. But by then I had come to a conclusion.

I could spend twenty thousand dollars for a building, or thirty thousand or fifty thousand, and, if I wanted to throw money around like that, I could get a building all right, but I wasn't going to do it. It would be degrading. It would be like buying up enough votes at a penny each—like they do in selecting the most popular girl in school to raise money for the PTA—to elect your own daughter the school queen. It would be a hollow victory, as far as I'm concerned. Besides, people lose respect for a man who buys extravagantly. Waiters don't respect flamboyant over-tippers. People will come a lot closer to respecting you for buying something for less than it's worth than more. If I couldn't get a building for somewhere close to what it was actually worth, there'd be no satisfaction in getting it. A man who doesn't respect the value of a dollar loses his worth as an editor in a town like Oat Hill and, I imagine, in a good many other towns, excusing possibly Washington.

I went back to my office and thought some more. I went home and kept thinking.

I was still thinking Sunday afternoon when I got in my car and drove around Oat Hill. I like to drive over the town, see what's going on, what improvements are taking place, and what houses are being allowed to run down. Oat Hill suits me as a town to live in; there are some pretty homes here along with some atrocious ones, the same as any place else you can name, such as Venice and Rome, and I get a lot of quiet enjoyment out of just driving over the place.

I had covered the eastern section of town and had come back to the courthouse square and turned south. I drove a couple of blocks and then turned west. About a block on west there was a group of vacant lots, a tract about two blocks square, mostly grown up in weeds. The tract is three blocks from the courthouse square, and why it had never built up is one of those oddities of growth. For some reason, mainly because a state highway cut the town east and west, people started building eastward and westward to have homes on a paved street in the days before Oat Hill had any paved residential streets, and the trend just continued. Most residential streets in town are now paved but the streets around this vacant tract were unimproved.

It belonged to a man living in St. Louis, J.W. Boushier. He had inherited it from his father who used to run the old Boushier Hotel in Oat Hill years ago, and I doubt if he'd seen it in fifteen or twenty years. Building lots in the tract just wouldn't sell on account of the dirt streets; the momentum of the town's growth was in the other direction, and the land just sat there.

As I bounced over the rough streets adjoining the tract, I was jolted into a thought I suppose was the most side-splitting I'd ever had. It beat that turtle deal ten to one and, besides, there wasn't a trace of deceit in it. The whole thought hit me ready-formed and I took a second good look at the tract of land and drove to my office at once. I got out my chart of the square and started figuring from an entirely different angle.

Once I got up and went to the front door and looked the old courthouse over, affectionately but with amusement. I haven't described the Altha County courthouse to you, but I need to now.

13

The Architectural Monstrosity

The Altha County courthouse was one of those monstrosities the architects unloaded on lots of counties in Texas seventy-five to a hundred years ago, somewhat like the Italian sculptor who sold the same original Civil War statue to towns all over the South. It had high peaked roofs, lots of gables, big lookout towers on each corner for no reason at all—all the Indians and wicked knights are gone—high-ceilinged rooms, wooden stairs, a basement that held water, and massive doors that let the north wind in. It's the type of structure college professors are always trying to preserve as a heritage from the past. Make that *glorious* past.

People had got used to the thing, like a man grown used to a dumb wife who's not even a good cook but who does sweep out once in a while.

Structurally, it was in bad shape. The roof leaked, the plaster was cracked and falling, the stairs were creaky, and the windows weren't tight. It was hard to heat in the winter and impossible to cool in the summer. Furthermore, the county was still paying for the thing. It's an odd fact, that while there are lots of good businessmen in Oat Hill who are sound thinkers from a dollar standpoint, running the county has always been turned over to the third-raters. Some states do the same thing, don't they Georgia? The county judge generally is a broken down school teacher, or a lawyer who couldn't make a living, or a druggist who went broke selling prescriptions on credit, elected out of a guilty conscience by those who owed him. The commissioners customarily are mediocre farmers with a prejudice against work for whom the $250-a-month salary has a strong appeal.

The county needed a new courthouse. The deeds and other legal records in the county clerk's office weren't safe in that fire trap, but most of the old-timers were satisfied; the thing hadn't burned yet and the tax rate was high enough. *All* tax rates are high enough.

After about an hour's figuring that Sunday afternoon, following my ride around town, I phoned Tom Webb and asked him if he'd come down to my office. It was about four o'clock.

"I know it's Sunday but I've got something I want you to do for me, that involves real estate; you might make a commission," I told him. He said he'd come right down. By four o'clock Sunday afternoon most people, even those with the most boring jobs, like store clerks and bank tellers, have had about all the leisure they can take and are looking forward to getting back to work Monday morning when they can think about something besides themselves. Man is most miserable when he has nothing to do. In about ten minutes Tom pulled up in front of the office and rattled the door.

"Tom," I said when he'd taken a chair across from my desk, "you know that tract of land over there, the Boushier tract, how much you reckon it can be bought for?"

"First, what in the world do you want with that?"

"Just figuring on something. Can you find out what it can be bought for?"

"I already know. I got it listed. Mr. Boushier's had it listed with me for years. Never been able to move a single lot on it. You mean you want to know what he'll take for the whole tract?"

"Yep."

"Well, there are 48 lots in that tract. He wants $150 a lot but I imagine he'd take a whole lot less for the entire tract. Believe he'd take $5,000 for all of it."

"Believe I'd give that much for it."

"O.K., I'll write him and see."

"No use writing. Just call him on the phone there."

"Phone him? You mean long distance to St. Louis? What you in such a hurry about?"

"Just want to know right away." When I see a course of action I want to take I like to get right on it. My stomach won't relax until I do. "Tell him I'll pay cash."

"Don't know whether I can get him on Sunday or not, but it won't hurt to try." Tom called the operator and placed the call. Wasn't five minutes till the phone rang back and Mr. Boushier was on the line in St. Louis. I have a notion people in St. Louis can get just as bored on Sunday afternoon as people in Oat Hill or Austin.

"Mr. Boushier? Tom Webb. I say this is Tom Webb, at Oat Hill. Oat Hill, Texas. Yeah. Oh, getting along all right. Folks fine. Uh, Mr. Boushier, what I called you about, you know those lots you have here in Oat Hill, I believe I've got a chance to sell the whole tract. Yeah, that's right, the whole tract. How much would you have to have? Oh, I don't know exactly, but I've got a man that seems pretty interested, if the price is right. Would you take $4,000?"

You can say this for Tom Webb, he doesn't let his thinking stray far from the profit motive when he's on a real estate deal.

"Sure," he continued, "they're worth more, but they just won't sell. This is the first nibble I've had in five years. Tell you what, would you take $4,500? Terms? Oh now, this is all cash. The man's ready to close." There was a pause. Personally I was ready to offer the full $5,000 or more but Tom was looking out for Tom. He'd already surmised there'd be a bonus in it for him from me if he got the price cut a little, and that plus what he'd make from Mr. Boushier on the standard five percent real estate dealer's commission would be a good day's work. He spoke into the phone again. "O.K. Fine. I think it's the thing to do. Think you're wise in selling. I'll get a deed fixed up and send it to your bank with a draft attached."

Tom hung up, smiled, and said, "Well, saved you $500.

"Thanks, Tom. I'll let you save me just $250. I'll split that $500 with you." Not only did I think he earned it, but I wanted Tom on my side and there's no better way to get a man on your side than to throw some business his way, or contribute to his campaign fund if he's running for office.

"O.K., if you say so," Tom said. "I'll get Jake Bowman to fix up the deed first thing in the morning."

"No, don't get Jake." I said. "Get Joe Darrel to do it. He needs the business more." Joe Darrel was a young lawyer just starting out and the older lawyers were making it as rough as they could on him. It's not unnatural. Ever notice how cows treat a strange one turned loose among them? Besides, I didn't want Jake Bowman knowing any more about my business than he could find out on his own.

"Tell him I want a complete abstract, too," I said. I wanted the title clear as daylight.

"It's none of my business," Tom said as he was leaving, "but I take it you've got a little oil money to spend?"

"Yeah, I got a little."

"What on earth are you going to do with those lots?"

"Tell you later on. There's going to be some selling involved and I want you to do it."

"You can count on me." As long as they get their five percent commission, real estate men don't care how many times they sell the same piece of property. Most preachers will marry the same couple over and over, won't they?

"By the way, Tom, sort of keep this quiet, will you?"

"Certainly."

He pulled the front door to after him and I rubbed my hands and went back to my chart.

14

Progress Hits Oat Hill

Now's as good a time as any to tell you what I was up to. I don't know if I can tell it so you won't think I've lost touch with reality, but I've tried to say that, given a lot of money, different people react in different ways. I've tried also to say that I hadn't been living in Oat Hill just because I couldn't afford to move away. The place suits me fine. If you're pretty well on to life on this earth, you can find that writing for 15,000 people in Altha County is as satisfying as writing for 100,000 or 5,000,000 in New York or all over the world. You probably get more reader reaction here than there; the income is about the same, and I can't be fired.

There are bigger towns, certainly, but size doesn't mean anything. Take the biggest city in this country, New York. Some New Yorkers consider themselves cosmopolites. They've been everywhere. They've seen everything. But did you know there are more folks in Oat Hill who've been to New York than there are folks in New York who've been to Oat Hill? In proportion to population, Oat Hill has just as many neon lights as New York, and they attract just as many candle flies. I suppose we have nearly as many murders in proportion to population as New York if you don't count those on the sidewalks—our sidewalks are safe. We read the same books and the same magazines, listen to the same radio news, fall asleep at the same television shows, see the same movies, read the same wire-service news. We don't have any art galleries, but the percentage of people in Oat Hill who haven't been to the New York Metropolitan Museum of Art is about as large as the percentage of New Yorkers who haven't. The percentage of those who have and aren't going back a second time is about the same, too. In the last presidential election Oat Hill and New York voted exactly alike, and I'm not bragging on either one. A steak in New York doesn't taste any better than a steak in Oat Hill, it only costs more. Our green salads have the same vegetables in them with the same salad dressings; the same brands of bourbon and scotch and vodka are available in both places, although for mixes we lean more to water or soda and don't go in much for tomato juice or soup.

I don't have the figure, I don't suppose anybody has, but I'll bet New York doesn't have a bit more adultery than Oat Hill, percentage-wise. Numerically, I guess they're ahead in the millions. Use of dope—well, I don't know but, by George, we've got some dopeheads here too, and occasionally one of our citizens goes nuts, although I'll concede we don't have any tall ledges for him to teeter on.

We have a fair share of crime. When somebody here steals something, it may not be as much but it's just as illegal. Our politicians are just as honest and just as venal as any they've got in New York. About the same proportion of people here belongs to a church and about the same proportion stays away. Before the thought of never-ending space, we're just as awed and baffled as the people of New York. The same sun comes up over Oat Hill in the morning and sets in the evening, and we've got a better look at it both times. In case of atomic war, the fall-out here will be just as deadly as any place else it drifts to. Waller Creek near Oat Hill won't compare with the Hudson in size, or in pollution—oh, occasionally a cow does misbehave in it—but it's just as wet. The trees on its banks are just as lush, and it beats the Hudson for turtles.

In short, life can be just as exciting, and just as dull, in Oat Hill, as in New York, Boston, San Francisco, or Dallas.

Therefore, maybe you'll understand when I say a million dollars had no power to change my way of life appreciably; and maybe you'll understand when I say that what I was going to do with a big wad of that cash was to have my own way, in my own way, in Oat Hill.

What I was fixing to do, since I couldn't get my own building on the courthouse square in a reasonable, business-like, economically

114

rational, personally dignified way, was *build a new courthouse square*.

This I figured would be the most exhilarating, most consternation-filling thing a man of my nature could do. Next to love, laughter is the best answer to the universe and, while this idea may not have been brimfull of love, it was overflowing with laughter.

Not only was I going to build a new courthouse square, I was going to make it pay me back what it cost. What a splendid idea! Every-time I thought about some of those old codgers sitting there on the old square hoarding their empty buildings while the town's main commerce moved to a new location I almost busted out laughing.

I don't know whether the sentiments and the motives that produced them are sociologically or morally sound, but I've noticed that few people in this life ever analyze their motives, ever truly follow their philosophies. They mostly drag their philosophies along behind. They act and then adopt a philosophy to fit and construct motives as afterthoughts, the way a man puts a false fireplace in a house already built without a chimney.

At any rate, I don't care how you analyze it, or where you put me in the sociological scale or the moral structure; that's what I was go-ing to do, and when a man has a million dollars in cash and isn't vio-lating the law, it's pretty hard to stop him. That's what I like about capitalism. It seems to be in tune with the true nature of the universe. I know that Jesus said you should give both your coat and your cloak to a chilly stranger, but Jesus never had a wife and two kids living a mile from the schoolhouse in Vermont.

Therefore, two weeks later, a lot of people in Oat Hill were mildly excited when a gang of workmen with dirt-moving equipment from Houston arrived on my tract of land and began operations. It hadn't taken long for the news to spread that I had bought the property. Ten minutes after the deed was recorded in the county clerk's office it was all over town, but to what use I intended to put it the people had to rely on their guesses.

Right off most people figured I was developing a subdivision, but others threw doubt on this idea when they saw how the streets were being laid out.

"First residential section I ever saw built in a square," Harry Gilcut said. "Go over there and look at it. Thing's laid off in a square, looks like one streets runs around the thing like the courthouse square right here."

"Aw, that's probably a newfangled idea, a sort of courtyard or playground in the center of the homes. Harold probably read it in a highbrow magazine." Jake Bowman distrusted anybody who read anything more than the *Dallas News* and maybe the *Reader's Digest* or the *Saturday Evening Post*. "If you ask me, Harold Smith is fixing to lose his shirt, or somebody's shirt."

"Yeah, but what's all that concrete mixing equipment for? He gonna build concrete streets?" somebody else asked.

"Them's probably gonna be tennis courts. Ain't you heard, all modern city additions got to have tennis courts."

"What I want to know is, who's financing Harold?" That was Jim Bowers. "Takes real money to do that kind of thing. Either somebody's got more money than he can handle or somebody is gonna hook somebody."

They didn't change the subject when I walked up.

"Harold, what in hell are you doing?" Harry Gilcut demanded. "We can't stand it. We've got to know."

"Oh, just doing a little improving. Place could stand a little, couldn't it? These old-timers been pioneering around here for fifty years and never did anything with those vacant lots. Time some newcomer took hold." This thing was going to get to fever pitch before I revealed any facts and, as an old turtle handler, I figured I knew how to let excitement mount.

"What are you using for money?" Jake Bowman never minded asking a blunt question.

"Why, money, Mr. Bowman," I said and smiled.

"Whose money?"

"Well, I guess it's no use telling these men here it's not yours."

Everybody guffawed, including Mr. Bowman, but he wasn't amused.

"Well, got to be getting on back to the *Gazette* office. Tomorrow's press day," I said and moved off. The crowd stood around to chew on it some more.

A week later a huge dragline moved in and started digging in the middle of the tract and the tennis court theory was abandoned in favor of a swimming pool.

"That's it!" Harry triumphed. "A swimming pool. Just what Oat Hill needs."

"But what the hell does he want a concrete street in the form of a square surrounding a swimming pool?" Jack Carter wanted to know.

"He's gonna charge for parking and pay for the swimming pool," Tom Hilbut suggested.

"To tell you the truth," I said (I was getting in the habit of happening up on these informal street corner discussions and adding fuel to the flames), "I'm having that hole dug in case we ever need to hold any mass funerals for some of the hardshells in this town. We got to be ready. There's some of these fellows we can't get under ground soon enough."

The swimming pool idea held out until the contractors started building forms and pouring concrete. "First swimming pool I ever saw with compartments in it, Harry," Jack Carter jibed.

"It's got me beat," Harry conceded. "One place for youngsters I can understand, but a swimming pool with eight sections and a sort of hall down the middle—don't ask me."

"Why, those are storage vaults," I put in. "Some people in this town too good to be buried in the ground, they got to be stored. When Resurrection Day comes, they got to be the first aboveground to pick out the choice spots to hoard."

When the brick masons started their work, all the previous theories were thrown out but what I wanted with a brick building, with that many rooms and a basement too, was a matter that only threw the town farther back into the dark.

Up to then I hadn't taken recognition of the project in the *Gazette*, but I figured it was time to tease the matter. I started poking fun at the enterprise, which worsened matters, as everybody knew I had tongue in cheek.

Maybe right here I ought to let you in on a little more. You're probably thinking the idea is too far-fetched and impractical for serious consideration, like giving television sets to an African province before it gets electricity or offering a course in sportsmanship to the fans of professional football.

I'll refer you to my chart. There are 300 feet on each side of my courthouse square, which means ten 30-foot building lots, or a total of 40 around the square. The last vacant lot around the Oat Hill courthouse, when the town was building and closing ranks 20 years ago, sold for $5,000. I figured my 40 lots would average at least $2,000 each, although I was going to try to beat that a little. If the more expensive corner lots—there were 8 of those—sold well, they ought to bring between $3,000 and $4,000 apiece, and the others should bring

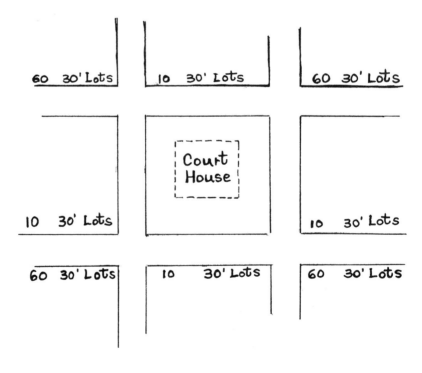

$2,000. But just say I was too optimistic and the whole thing averaged $2,000 per lot. That's $80,000, less the price of one for me. Now you've got to remember I bought four full blocks of land, so that gives me control also of the lots on the streets leading onto the square, 160 of them, each 30 feet wide (ten lots to the block, one side of the street, but the streets have two sides, so each street would have 20 lots, and 20 times 8 is 160). For these lots, which naturally would be slow moving, I figured eventually I'd get $500 each, which also is $80,000. These, of course, would be long-term propositions but when you've got plenty of money long terms are fine, even better than short terms when you figure the interest.

Now if you figure up the possible lot sales you'll see the land around the square and on the adjoining streets, if the thing panned out, would bring a total of $160,000.

The original land cost me $4,750. Paving the street around the square and two blocks off on each side came to $65,000.

The courthouse, of simple but durable design, with a flat top and no wasteful domes, peaks, battlements, and high ceilings, was costing me $90,000, and there was a lot-sale possibility of $160,000 or slightly more. I would wind up with three or four lots of my own, including one on the square. One was all I wanted on the square. Clearly, the sale of lots could pay for the entire project.

As the courthouse building neared completion the town continued guessing. Everything was suggested from a library to a hotel to a civic center to a school building to plain insanity. The best rumor by now, which I'd aided and abetted, was that the building was sort of a civic center, with a library. The courtroom occupying most of the upstairs, I had implied, was a theatre for the production of amateur plays, although I never came right out and said so. As far as I'm concerned, an amateur play is about like an amateur singer. Nobody in his right mind can stand either, although I'll concede there never was an Oat Hill school play produced that the *Gazette* didn't refer to as a smash hit, a critical judgment considered fair by the parents of every boy and girl in the cast.

As construction moved on, I planted more hints and got the rumors

119

going. It's no harder to get a rumor going in Oat Hill than it is in the congressional corridors in Washington or the diplomatic circles of the world.

Luckily, at about this time, the Women's Reading Club of Oat Hill, which served the fanciest sandwiches and read the fewest books, had come out for a new courthouse for Altha County.

The idea was born when Mrs. Clarence Millington, president of the club, sprained her ankle when she broke through a treadway while hoisting her ponderous bulk slowly up the stairs to the courtroom.

What Mrs. Millington was climbing the stairs for was to present a petition to the Commissioners Court asking that everybody in Oat Hill and all of Altha County plant crape myrtle around his home. This place then could be called the Crape Myrtle Center of Texas and it would be nice, Mrs. Millington explained, carrying on like a trooper, despite the pain in her ankle.

Every place needs a reputation of some sort. New York is known as the Financial and Cultural Center. There's a portion of Galveston known as the Red-light Center. What's the matter with a Crape Myrtle Center?

The creaky stairway and the sprained ankle got Mrs. Millington to thinking, and it wasn't long before the Women's Reading Club adopted a new courthouse as its main literary project.

Several other organizations took up the cry, like the Baptist Sunday School's Sunshine Class and the Epworth League of the Methodist Church and, you can depend on it, the *Gazette* gave it all the publicity it would stand and maybe a little more.

By the time Mrs. Millington's ankle splint was removed and she was, so to speak, stripped for action, the battle was on. Most of the women and about a third of the men were in favor of a new courthouse, but most of the property owners—the old codgers around the square, the residential rent-house owners, and the bigger landowners—were violently opposed.

"What you need a new courthouse for?" Jake Bowman growled. "This one's good enough to try all the criminals we got. Maybe needs a little sprucing up here and there, but a new courthouse? As high as things are? Where'd you get the money? County's already in debt."

When an architect from Houston addressed the Oat Hill Garden Club on modern trends in architecture and called the Altha County courthouse an "architectural abomination," the *Gazette* headlined the story. The members of the Reading Club, most of whom were members of the Garden Club too, laid down their bridge cards and sandwiches and appeared before the Commissioner's Court in a body demanding a new courthouse.

County Judge DeWitt Shelton explained to the women that the county was sort of hard up and had no way to build a new courthouse except by tax bonds, and voting bonds was up to the people. Personally, Judge Shelton wanted a new courthouse, the same as a renter is always in favor of the landlord's fixing up the place, although in this case the judge wasn't even paying rent. I don't know why taxpayers haven't thought of charging office holders office rent.

Carolyn, who had now developed into a pretty good newspaper reporter, was on hand to report the demands of the women for the *Gazette*, and I thought it was worth a three-column headline at the top of the front page: OAT HILL WOMEN DEMAND NEW COURTHOUSE.

The issue was beginning to boil satisfactorily, and I figured it was time to strike. My building project was completed.

At the next meeting of the Commissioners Court, I was on hand and asked DeWitt if I could say a few words. What I said was that I had something to show the court and wondered if the members would walk over to my so-called civic center and take a look. I assured them it affected them vitally. By the way, I ought to say I kept the new courthouse locked tight, having even hired a guard to keep visitors out.

We all went in a body to the center, and I unlocked the front door and stood aside while the court went in. I showed them the basement rooms without saying much, then led the way up the stairs, which were concrete and not likely to give way with Mrs. Millington, regardless of her sandwich intake, and threw open the doors to the big room.

"What I want to know, Harold, is what in hell is this?" The judge couldn't hold in any longer.

"What does it look like, Judge?"

"Well, to tell the truth, it looks sort of like a courtroom."

"Well, Judge," I said, pausing a little for dramatic effect, "that's exactly what it is."

"Well, what—? who's—?"

"Judge, what would you say if I told you this is a courthouse?"

"I'd say it's a mighty nice one, but one of the damned screwiest things I ever heard of. What in hell is it for?"

"Why, it's to use." I tried to sound as though I was answering somebody who'd asked me what I was going to do with a new automobile.

"For *who* to use?" The judge's mouth was gaping about as much as the Commissioners'.

"Gentlemen," I said, "let's go in here." I led them to a room adjoining the courtroom and asked them to take seats around a conference table, the only furniture in the building.

"This," I continued when they were seated, awed like school boys in a brand new school building whose walls are not yet marked with handprints, "is the commissioners' room. You can see it adjoins the main courtroom, convenient for hearing large crowds on occasion."

"Yeah, but what's it for?" Commissioner Haskel Pettigrew, from the east end of the county, was a brusque man, known as the watch dog of the county treasury except when his precinct was up for an appropriation, the same as all congressmen. He wanted me to come to the point.

"Why, it's for you and the rest of the commissioners, and for the people of Altha County," I said.

"I don't think we're in the market," he said.

"Who said anything about selling it?"

"You can't *rent* a courthouse."

"Who said anything about renting it?"

"Well, what do you mean . . .?"

"I mean, gentlemen, I want to *give* you this courthouse." It was like a banker's putting on his hat and walking up to the tellers and telling them he was giving them the bank and goodbye.

"You mean you are hauling off and giving this courthouse, free of cost, with no strings attached, to Altha County?" Judge Shelton asked.

"That's right. Absolutely free of charge. No bonded indebtedness. But there's one string."

"What's that?"

"You'll have to use it."

"What do you mean?"

"I mean you'll have to use it. You'll have to move your furniture and fixtures out of the other courthouse, move all the officeholders, the tax assessor-collector, the sheriff, the county clerk, all of them, over here. That's all."

"About the craziest thing I ever heard of, but I'm just crazy enough to accept it," the judge said.

The others were joining in until Commissioner Pettigrew advised caution. "Sounds like a mighty good proposition to me, but let's wait a little while. Better sound out the people."

That sounded reasonable to me, or cautious, which is the same thing to a politician. The commissioners got up and walked around inspecting the rest of the building, which was fireproof throughout and—this I figured would be the clincher—air-conditioned.

Electrified is the word to describe the people of Oat Hill and Altha County when the *Gazette* came out that week with the announcement that I had offered a brand new courthouse free of charge to the county.

People poured into my office congratulating me, asking me how I did it. Where'd I get the money? Some came just to stare and ponder my sanity.

Of course it didn't take long for the implications to sink in on the property owners around the square.

"You recognize what he's up to?" Jake Bowman asked Jim Bowers. "You seen what it could do to us?"

"I certainly have. I don't understand how he got the money to do it, but if the courthouse shows up in that new location, the old courthouse ain't gonna be the only thing that's vacant around here. It's gonna split this town half in two. Ain't no way to keep some businesses from locating over there."

"That's just what I'd figured already. We got to fight this thing."

"You tell me how. You're not in much shape to fight. Already said we couldn't afford to build a new courthouse here. There's gonna be an avalanche of demand to accept this free one. What do you think the country people are gonna say? You know blamed well they'll be in favor of accepting the new one. What do they care how much we've got invested in our property here?"

"We've got to get out an injunction against it."

"Injunction, hell. Where's the judge who'd say the people ought to pay for a new courthouse instead of accepting one free? Even the Supreme Court would vote unanimous on that."

The two parted, agreeing they'd call a meeting of the property owners to see what could be done.

15

Doors Flapping in the Wind

"Harold, you sure got the hornets flying!" Tom Webb came into my office rubbing his hands. "Never saw so many worried old codgers."

"What're they worrying about? They still got their buildings."

Tom grinned and pulled up a chair. "What's the next step?"

I had phoned him to come over. "Well, the next step involves you. You got a lot of selling to do. I'm the contented owner of 200 lots, 40 around the new courthouse, and 160 on the streets leading onto it."

Tom shifted his weight in his chair and leaned forward. Say what you please, but nothing makes a painter, a writer, a violinist, or a real estate man happier than the thought of some money rolling in.

"Now, Tom, here's the map of the layout. Prices are marked on the lots. Only restrictions are that only fireproof buildings, concrete or brick construction, can go up. Corner lots are worth $3,500; all the rest around the square are worth $2,000. I've got four lots reserved for myself; one on the square, three on the side streets. You can pick out one for yourself, if you want to. Figure your commissions ought to be enough to pay for a lot and put up a building too, if you want one. There's just one thing. Everybody who owns a building on the present courthouse square can have the privilege of buying a lot duplicating his old location. Limit one to a customer. Be sort of interesting to have the new square match up with the old one."

Tom studied the map a little while, picked out a lot in the middle of the block on the north side of the square and marked it sold.

"Gonna mark yours sold too," he said. "Makes it look like we're doing business."

"Now you don't have to get cash, Tom. Matter of fact, you shouldn't even complete the sale, just sell options. I'll put up the deed, the buyer puts up a cash deposit, we put them in escrow in the bank, and the sale is contingent on the people of Altha County accepting the free courthouse. If the county doesn't accept it, then the buyer's money will be returned. You reckon they're going to accept it?"

"Of course they are. You ever hear of a country on earth turning down foreign aid?"

Tom picked up the map and left. That was about nine o'clock in the morning. By noon he was back in the office.

"Say, this is fun," he beamed. "Already sold eight lots. Got young Joe to type up a whole stack of options, ready to fill in, and the people who're renting buildings are hot to buy."

"By the way, Tom, I forgot to tell you. Don't sell to any outsiders yet. We're going to limit sales to local people first."

That week's *Gazette* carried a full-page ad announcing the sale of lots around the "proposed" new courthouse square. It explained that for the next two weeks the sale would be limited to local people already in business or living in Oat Hill and Altha County, after which outside capital would be invited to buy. I even bought the space and ran the same page ad in Editor Clayton Martin's *News*. Didn't need to but when a man has plenty of money it's easy to be generous. Besides, editors in Oat Hill, or Dallas, rarely take strong stands against firms that buy page ads.

I tell you, business was humming. The people were clamoring to accept the courthouse; the old-square owners were fuming and planning, and the lots were selling fast. By the middle of the second week practically all the lots around the square and about a third of the lots on the adjoining streets were sold. Whatever you say about some of the old timers, they weren't fools. Old Jake Bowman and Jim Bowers and three or four others bought lots themselves, using agents, so their names wouldn't show up in the transaction.

By this time Judge Shelton and the Commissioners Court were

convinced that the people were in favor of accepting a free courthouse and the court duly voted to accept it. There were some legal technicalities involved over what to do with the old courthouse but, since the problem was without precedent, the only ruling Judge Shelton could get from the attorney general of Texas was that there certainly wasn't anything unlawful about being given a free courthouse and letting the old one stand abandoned, its doors flapping in the wind.

By this time the daily papers in the state were playing the thing up pretty big. After the two-week local sale period, outsiders quickly bought up the remaining lots around the square and a good many of those on the connecting streets. Several farmers and ranchers in the county bought the cheaper lots, just as investments.

At the end of four weeks enough lots had been sold to total $145,-000, and I still had about $30,000 worth to be sold in the years ahead. Some of the lots, after the courthouse was formally accepted and the officeholders moved in, were paid for in cash, others on long terms, but the paper was good. While I had been willing to lose some money on the deal, it began to look like I actually was going to make some. Nothing increases a man's perspicacity like a million dollars of surplus capital. It helps him see more opportunities. That's the reason the insurance companies, if not the Arabs, may own this country some day, if we don't watch it.

By now construction was going on. The *Gazette* building was half finished. To encourage progress, I had two other buildings going up on my other lots. By using common walls between the buildings and pouring one great slab of concrete in each block for a continuous, rat-proof floor, owners found they could construct buildings a lot cheaper than they could by the old way, putting up a building every few years, each one with new walls and floors to itself. In a year's time the courthouse square was lined with buildings on all sides, and stores were thriving.

I never could figure out what could be done with the old courthouse and the buildings surrounding it. The buildings are still there, and they certainly look gaunt and forgotten. Lots of tourists come by to drive around the old square and chuckle, but there's no money in that. Jake Bowman held out to the last, continuing to practice law in his lonesome office upstairs over his vacant building on the west side of the old square. But he finally gave in and moved to his new building, saying he guessed he knew when he was whipped.

Maybe I shouldn't have done it, but if the builders of empire had felt that way the Indians would still be running this country. The air and the streams might have stayed pure, but it's too late to go back. Might as well try to uninvent the atom bomb.

As for the people of Oat Hill, they seem as happy and normal as it's given man to be. Just the other day a young man wanting to put in a new auto supply store was complaining he couldn't buy a building on the courthouse square. Said a newcomer hasn't got a chance here. I guess I'm getting old. I told him it wasn't any skin off my back.

The 2000-Mile Turtle, tenth book produced by Madrona Press, has been printed on Warren's Olde Style white wove. Type is eleven-point Times Roman, three-point leaded, set on Merganthaler's V-I-P Phototypesetter by G & S Typesetters. Printing by offset lithography was done by Capital Printing Company.

Sketches by Barbara Embree
Turtle Drawings by William A. Seymour

MADRONA PRESS, INC.
AUSTIN, TEXAS